Poultry
Waterfowl Problems

by
Michael Roberts

Edited by
Sara Roadnight

Photographs and Illustrations by
Michael Roberts & Sara Roadnight

POULTRY & WATERFOWL PROBLEMS

INTRODUCTION 3

FOREWORD 4

DISEASES & PROBLEMS OF HENS AND BANTAMS 5

DISEASE & PROBLEMS OF DUCKS & GEESE 42

DISEASE & PROBLEMS OF TURKEYS 56

WHAT CAN I CATCH FROM MY BIRDS ? 68

SIGNS OF GOOD HEALTH 70

WHAT TO CHECK WHEN CONFRONTED WITH A SICK BIRD 71

DROPPINGS 73

STRESS 74

KILLING BIRDS 76

GENERAL NOTES 78

VETERINARY TERMS / PLAIN ENGLISH 81

LIST OF VETS 84

INTRODUCTION

This book has been written with first hand experience. If there are subjects that I have had no experience of, then I have obtained information from people who I know do have relevant experience. A few people I have met become quite paranoid about their birds health. I must say that birds kept in the right conditions are very robust, but if you have a problem don't contact me, just consult your local avian vet, a list of whom is to be found at the back of the book.

The author and publisher cannot be held responsible for any action taken as a result of reading this book, and medicines should at all times be used in accordance with the manufacturer's instructions or on the advice of your veterinary surgeon.

My thanks to Jerry Bailey Watts for his assistance.

© 1998 MICHAEL ROBERTS
PUBLISHED BY DOMESTIC FOWL RESEARCH.
ISBN 978 094787026 3

FOREWORD

We have tried to keep this book as simple as possible while at the same time maintaining a veterinary feel to it, as books of this nature are so often confusing and unintelligible to the ordinary person.

This book does not deal with all the diseases and complaints found in poultry and waterfowl but only the ones you are more likely to encounter. Having said that of course, Murphy's Law will probably mean that your birds develop something most unusual that we have not covered! But if you are unsure what your birds are suffering from, contact your local avian vet. There is a list at the back of this book.

When I first started in poultry some 24 years ago, most of the specialist books were talking about roup, croup, canker, going light and coxy; but information on diseases and their treatments has moved on since then.

We will not be dealing with problems encountered with intensively reared birds, of which we have no experience. We have tried to design this book to help you understand and recognize the disease or problem, how to treat it and how to avoid it. Sometimes it is very difficult to recognize a complaint, as it may be several rolled into one, so be careful and don't jump to any hasty conclusions.

A number of diseases and problems arise from simple management faults such as lack of hygiene or incorrect ventilation, heating, feeding and/or stress; but if you adhere to a regular schedule of management most of these problems will not occur.

If you are a newcomer to chickens or waterfowl and you read this book, don't be put off. Most birds are very robust and you are unlikely to see many of the problems mentioned.

It is very gratifying to see the number of these books going out to veterinary surgeries. I have no veterinary qualifications but, like anyone who works closely with birds or animals, I find that as you get to know them you become familiar with their ways and the state of their health. You will quickly become aware of symptoms if they arise, and will learn how to treat them with both drugs and herbal remedies.

**MICHAEL ROBERTS AND SARA ROADNIGHT,
KENNERLEIGH, DEVON**

HENS AND BANTAMS

I have not listed all the diseases and problems, but only the ones you are likely to encounter, and some of these I hope you will never see. I have tried to put them into a simple table, which I hope will not confuse you.

B =	CAUSED BY A BACTERIA	C =	CHICK 1-4 weeks
V =	CAUSED BY A VIRUS	G =	GROWER 5–18 weeks
F =	CAUSED BY A FUNGUS	A =	ADULT 19+ weeks
P =	CAUSED BY A PROTOZOA		

DISEASE	TYPE OF DISEASE	AGE OF SUSCEPTIBILITY			PAGE
Aspergillosis	F	C	G	A	6
Avian diphtheria	V	C	G	A	7
Avian tuberculosis	B			A	7
Blackhead	P		G	A	8
Coccidiosis	P	C	G	A	9
E-Coli	B	C	G	A	10
Favus	P		G	A	10
Fowl cholera	B	C	G	A	11
Infectious bronchitis	V		G	A	11
Leucosis	V		G	A	12
Mareks	V		G	A	13
Mycoplasma	B		G	A	15
Newcastle disease	V	C	G	A	16
Psittacosis	B		G	A	17
Salmonella	B	C	G	A	18
Vent gleet	B		G	A	19
Worms	P		G	A	19

Problems encountered in Hens and Bantams

	Page			Page
Altitude	21		Heart Problems	30
Beak Deformity	21		Mites, Northern Fowl	31
Blindness	21		Mites, Red	31
Breastbone Deformities	22		Moulting	32
Bumble Foot	22		Nutritional Disorders	33
Cannibalism	22		Poison	34
Choking	23		Prolapse	34
Cock Damage	24		Rings	35
Curly Toe	24		Roach Back	35
Ear Infection	25		Scaley Leg	36
Eggs	26		Sex Change	37
Egg Bound	26		Sour Crop	37
Egg Eating	27		Stress	38
Feather Loss	27		Suffocation	39
Feather Pecking	27		Toe Balls	40
Fleas & Lice	28		Waterbelly	40
Fox Bites	29		Wing Clipping	41
Frost Bite	29		Woodshavings	41

MORTALITY: Is expressed as the number of birds in your flock which are likely to die from the disorder. LOW is 10% and less, MEDIUM is 50% and less, HIGH is 50% and above.

<u>ASPERGILLOSIS</u> - This is a disease of bad management.

SIGNS - Birds stretching their necks to breathe; hoarse breathing noise; dead birds; birds dying within 24 hours.

CAUSE - A fungus called Aspergillosis fumigatus which is found everywhere, but especially in warm damp conditions, like wet shavings, hay, or straw. A build up will occur usually in litter which is not cleaned out regularly, or when a drinker leaks, or water is splashed about. Stale food can also be a cause.

PREVENTION - Clean all your rearing equipment, and ensure that there is always fresh litter. People often rear on weld mesh, with droppings trays underneath, just in order to avoid this disease.

TREATMENT - None, just prevention with good management and hygiene.

MORTALITY - Low to medium.

AVIAN DIPHTHERIA (fowl pox or canker)

I remember seeing this disease when I was a boy. It is now rare.

SIGNS - One sign is external, with the bird developing yellowish lumps on the comb which turn into crusty warts covering the head, and sometimes the feet and legs. The second, and more common sign is the bird gasping for air. Look inside the mouth and the top of the throat and you will see yellow cheesy growths which will eventually cause the death of the bird as it won't be able to breathe or eat.

CAUSE - This is the fowl pox virus, which is normally seen in autumn and winter. The disease is spread through cuts and abrasions, fleas, lice and sometimes mosquitoes. It is seen at all ages but particularly between 6-12 months

PREVENTION - This is again a disease of poor management and overstocking. A good hygiene programme together with lower stocking densities would overcome this.

TREATMENT - This disease is rare, but you should be aware of it, particularly if you have a bird straining for breath. This could be Avian diphtheria. It could also be Gapes, but is more likely to be something stuck in the windpipe. There is a vaccine against this, but you would have to check with your vet.

MORTALITY - Medium.

This poor bird is choking to death with a build up of cheesy substance in the throat and mouth. This is AVIAN DIPTHERIA.

AVIAN TUBERCULOSIS

SIGNS - Normally seen in older birds. The birds look off colour for a long time, don't lay and gradually become weaker and thinner, and die. Only a post-mortem will reveal this.

CAUSE - The Mycobacterium avium is spread by contact with infected birds, soil, hands, feet, housing, crates and wild birds. It is rare in chickens, but if your birds contract this disease, it can take a long time to clear up.

PREVENTION - There isn't any. Birds can be tested for T.B. with an injection of avian tuberculin into the right or left wattle. If, after 48 hours there is no reaction, the birds are clear. If the wattle swells and feels hot to the touch, then the bird is a reactor, and should be culled. This is all done by your local vet, but the test is not 100% accurate. Once tested, the birds should be moved to a clean or sterilised house.

TREATMENT - There is none.

MORTALITY - High.

BLACKHEAD (Histomoniasis)

SIGNS - Birds looking listless, uninterested in life or food, losing weight, and often with bright yellow diarrhoea.

CAUSE - Blackhead has nothing to do with the head going black, but it is a disease of the caecal tracts and liver. It is caused by a minute parasite called Histomonas meleagridis which is spread by a roundworm called Heterakis, which is mainly found in the caecal tracts. The eggs of this roundworm, carrying the parasite Histomonas, are taken up by the bird and once inside, Histomonas multiplies rapidly, causing severe damage to the caecal tracts and liver, hence the bright yellow droppings. Meanwhile the bird begins to lose weight and interest in life and eventually dies of blood poisoning due to peritonitis, (the wall of the gut having been pierced). One of the problems of this disease is that the more affected round-worm eggs the birds produce, the worse the situation becomes, as the eggs will be passed through more and more birds and earthworms; this can mean that the disease sometimes remains in the ground for several years.

PREVENTION - Apart from moving your birds to fresh ground, there is none. If you are running chickens and turkeys together there is a chance of seeing Blackhead in evidence, but this is normally quite rare. Many people will tell you that you can't run chickens and turkeys together on a free range basis, but I have done so for 22 years, and have found that the birds do build up an immunity to the disease.

TREATMENT - Dimetridazole (Emtryl or Harkanker) in the drinking water. Remove all other drinking water and ensure that the birds don't have access to puddles etc. Within 24 hours there is a marked improvement in the birds and an interest in food once again.

At the moment, the madmen from Brussels are trying to ban Dimetridazole, and there is no safe substitute. I am not sure what the game farmers and turkey producers will do if it is banned.

MORTALITY - Low.

To take a bird's temperature, insert the thermometer in the vent; the normal temperature of a hen is 103 degrees.

COCCIDIOSIS (Coxy)

SIGNS - Milky white diarrhoea, sometimes with blood in it, mopey birds, poor growth, thirsty, sudden death especially at night. Young stock are particularly vulnerable between 3 - 8 weeks, but this can affect some birds at any age.

CAUSE - This is a protozoan parasite, of which there are many different types (34!). The main group is Eimeria of which seven different kinds occur in hens. The Eimeria eggs (or oocysts) are passed out in the droppings (an infected bird can produce millions of eggs). They then need warm and damp conditions in which to develop, hence Coccidiosis tends to occur more in the autumn, or during periods of wet weather in the summer. (Coxy can also be found in damp litter indoors). The eggs, or oocysts, are then picked up by other hens, and take up residence in the small intestine, duodenum and caecal tracts, where they develop and multiply. The outcome for the bird will depend on the variety or varieties of Coccidiae and the numbers involved. Stress plays a part here too: a low immune system can lead to rapid death.

This is a typical sight of birds dead or dying from COCCIDIOSIS; the weak birds have been smothered by the healthier birds during the night and in the process have lost feathers on their breasts or backs.

PREVENTION - If you are rearing on grass, there is nothing you can do, except ensure your young birds are well on in the autumn, i.e. hatch early: March, April or May, and keep the grass as short as you can; Coxy loves long wet grass. The older the young stock, the greater the immunity they will have, thus it is more often young birds which die of this disease. Late birds can be reared on slats or wire mesh to avoid this problem, or dry litter such as shavings.

TREATMENT - The most effective treatment is a drug called Baytox. This usually clears it up, but you will continue to lose a few more birds despite the treatment. I am against in-feed anti-coccidiosis medicines (coccidiostats) as I believe that it is better to treat your birds with the correct drug at the right time, rather than feed them continually with a suppressant. Most commercial organisations use Paracox in the drinking water when the chicks are seven days old. This is given for seven days.

MORTALITY - Can be high.

E-COLI (Colibacillosis)

SIGNS - In chicks, the bird(s) stands around often apart from the rest of the group, hunched and cheeping. (The sound is more 'weep' 'weep'). The bird is not interested in food or water, and the wings appear to be too large for the body. There is also a sweet/sour smell. In larger and adult birds, E-coli shows itself as birds being off colour and often with runny brown droppings

CAUSE - This is a complex set of microbes which normally live harmoniously in the intestines. When poor hygiene, stale food, stress, or some other problem like Coccidiosis or Mycoplasma are present, the E-coli bacteria go into overdrive, resulting in the death of the bird, normally from blood poisoning.

PREVENTION - This is a disease caused by slack management. You must have a thorough programme of cleaning out with a proper disinfectant, not only in the incubator, but right the way through the rearing and breeding system. Stale food (i.e. out of date food), and stress are other factors affecting E-coli outbreaks.

TREATMENT - Probiotics (Protexin) either in the food or the water will clear up E-coli in chicks, and will work for older birds providing nothing else has latched on, such as Coccidiosis or Mycoplasma. If this is the case you may have to treat the other complaint first. A good tip for chicks is to lightly spray them and their surroundings with Virkon 'S' each day. This not only controls any pathogens and bacteria but also promotes feather growth.

MORTALITY - Low to medium.

FAVUS

SIGNS - A whitish crusty or scaley fungus like growth around the face and wattles of the bird. I only put this in because of a recent magazine article, where no one knew what the disease was. It is very rare in this country.

CAUSE - Favus is a ringworm on poultry and smells very offensive. This disease is seen mainly in the tropics.

PREVENTION - None. I would not expect anyone to allow their birds to get into this condition.

TREATMENT - There is a treatment, but because the disease is contagious to humans, (zoonotic), it is best to cull the bird(s). Use gloves when handling any birds with this disease.

FOWL CHOLERA

This is another zoonotic disease. Although rare, it is worth being aware of; it is also notifiable. Turkeys are more susceptible than chickens

This bird is very typical of a sick bird: mopey, cold looking, not interested in food, wings seeming slightly too long for the body, and typical hedgehog feathers on the top of the head, denoting a headache. This is the typical appearance of a bird pulled down by one disease, and one or two other diseases or problems jumping on the bandwagon.

SIGNS - This is a rare disease now, so it is unlikely that your birds will contact it, but it is sensible to know about it and be able to recognise it. Outbreaks occur mainly during heat waves and when birds are stressed by heat. The birds look mopey with a discharge from the nostrils and watery green or white diarrhoea, and they die rather quickly with the severe form of the disease. In the less severe or chronic form, mortality is less, birds appear to have swollen heads and breathe with difficulty.

CAUSE - It is caused by a bacteria called Pasteurella multocida which comes in various strains. Some of you may recall the famous French scientist called Louis Pasteur and his struggle to find a vaccine against Smallpox; this bacteria was one of several to be named after him. The disease is transmitted from bird to bird by contamination from a carrier bird, wild birds or vermin and by water, people, equipment, food bags, vehicles, etc. As you can see, it is very contagious.

PREVENTION - There is none. Listen to any reports of outbreaks in your area, and be careful where you buy your stock. Good husbandry and cleaning programmes are essential.

TREATMENT - Although it can be treated with sulphur based drugs like Sulphamezathine, the problem remains that your birds may become carriers. As it is a notifiable disease, there is a total slaughter programme.

MORTALITY - In the severe form it is high, but otherwise mortality is low to medium.

INFECTIOUS BRONCHITIS

Unfortunately, I.B. as it is commonly called in the commercial world, is no longer a disease peculiar to commercial outfits, but is now finding its way into small domestic flocks.

SIGNS - With young birds, the first signs are gasping, snicking and rattling which can be further complicated by E-Coli and Mycoplasma (smell!) The birds look mopey and cold and lose condition quickly as they are not interested in food. This can develop into another strain of the virus called Nephrophilia which affects the kidneys and causes the birds to drink more, resulting in rather runny, watery droppings. This virus has a higher mortality rate, and young cock birds seem more prone to this disease then hens. In laying birds, the main signs to look out for, apart from the wheezing and snicking, are a drop in egg production, misshapen eggs, loss of pigmentation particularly in brown eggs, and poor quality egg shells. Eggs appear rough in texture. Crack one open and you will notice the white is watery, and the yolk slides around in the white instead of being firmly in one place.

CAUSE - Infectious Bronchitis is a virus from the Coronavirus family, and is normally spread from bird to bird by breathing, but can be spread on equipment and the stockman's clothing.

PREVENTION - Good disinfectants will knock out this virus, but it is best to clean out the affected batch or flock of birds because if the young hens do recover, they will carry immunity to the disease, but they may have damaged their fallopian tubes in the process, which in turn will cause them to lay misshapen eggs.

TREATMENT - If a post-mortem has proved that your birds have I.B. it is easily treated by vaccinating your young chicks.

MORTALITY - Low to medium.

LEUCOSIS

SIGNS - Similar symptoms to Mareks, and often confused with Mareks disease. Occasional healthy birds suddenly dying or looking off colour, not many birds seem to be affected. Mainly in birds of 18 weeks.

CAUSE - Like Mareks this is a carcinogenic disease but fortunately it is not very common. The signs are an enlargement of the spleen and liver. There are several types of Leucosis. This disease is passed on through the egg.

PREVENTION - There is none.

TREATMENT - There is none. As with Mareks, rear your young stock away from adult birds.

MORTALITY - Is low.

Years ago, when I was in Atlanta, USA for a World Poultry Fair, I sat next to an Egyptian professor of poultry science. I discovered from him that there was still an old Egyptian breed of fowl call the Fayoumi in Egypt, and I asked him to bring me over some eggs the next time he was in London. I then thought no more of it until one day I had a call from Heathrow Airport (London) to say the professor had arrived and he had my eggs. I dashed over and collected them, put them through my quarantine centre, and informed the Ministry of Agriculture. Of course they flipped and all the young birds which had hatched had to be blood tested twice. The second time, I had a call from the Ministry saying that as the birds had got <u>Newcastle Disease</u> they were coming to kill all of those in quarantine and all the rest of my collection!! I told them that I thought they were mistaken as all the birds looked perfectly healthy to me.

The second time they sent a vet who didn't know how to draw blood from a bird (there is a large vein under the wing). They then telephoned back to say that they had got the blood samples mixed up in the laboratory!!! The reason I mention Fayoumis is that they are one of the few breeds which are resistant to Leucosis

<u>MAREKS DISEASE</u> or Fowl Paralysis

SIGNS - These are very variable which makes this disease sometimes difficult to diagnose without a post-mortem. There may be dead birds between the ages of 6 weeks to 20 weeks, birds with legs stretched out unable to walk or using a wing as a crutch, or birds just looking off colour and not growing. Sometimes they are ravenously hungry and very thin, sometimes gaping, and it appears that mainly hen birds are affected.

CAUSES - Mareks is a stress disease, and is caused by a herpes virus. There are two forms, classical which affects the legs and wings, and acute Mareks which affects various organs such as the liver, kidneys, lungs, spleen or heart, but it is sometimes difficult to differentiate between the two. The

One of the classic poses for MAREKS DISEASE, one leg stretched out in front and the other behind, although this is not always seen in Mareks disease.

important thing to realise is that the disease is spread by feather dust which is inhaled by the chick or grower. The incubation time is long, hence good birds dying at 18 weeks old and more. Certain ornamental breeds such as Hamburgs, Sebrights and Silkies seem to be genetically more prone to catching Mareks, and although this has not been proved it remains a possibility.

Once a hen reaches laying age it rarely dies of Mareks and can be said to be immune but it can still remain a carrier of the virus. Mareks can be spread by wild birds.

PREVENTION - Never mix adult birds with chicks or growers and never mix different age batches of young birds together. Once the chicks have been vaccinated keep them isolated for at least five weeks, (that is if you have Mareks disease). Spray your chicks and growers and their surroundings daily with a fine mist of Virkon 'S' and don't swap drinkers and feeders. Vacuum the inside of the rearing building regularly to remove all dust and cobwebs etc. It helps to keep the dust levels down if you line everything with polythene sheeting. Remember, if a bird is immune or resistant to Mareks, it is still a carrier of the virus, so it is fine with other <u>adult</u> birds but <u>death</u> to youngstock.

TREATMENT - Vaccination at day old, or a long process of breeding immune birds. Most people go for the former. Remember, vaccination is not 100% effective so it takes a couple of seasons to rid yourself of the disease, but it can be done with rigorous hygiene and careful planning.

The vaccination technique with Marexine from Intervet is as follows:

Take the vial of vaccine from the fridge. Add 2ml of dilutant to the vaccine with the syringe. It fizzes. Draw out the vaccine and dilutant mixture with the syringe and inject it into the bottle of dilutant. Repeat this until the vaccine vial is empty.

Put the mixture into the injection gun or injection syringe. If you are using 1000 dose and 1000 dilutant, inject 0.1 into the chick, if you are using 1000 dose and 2000 dilutant inject 0.2 into the chick. Adjust the injection gun accordingly. The first dose can be increased to 0.2ml safely, and if you have some vaccine mixture over, three week old chicks can be given a repeat injection.

Remember:

This Dorking chick is being injected against MAREKS DISEASE. Injections at day old can take place under the skin on the neck, thigh or wing.

- use the vaccine within <u>1½ hours</u>

- chicks must be day-old for the vaccine to work

- inject into the neck, wing or thigh under the skin

- isolate chicks for 3 to 4 weeks: Mareks is spread by feather dust

- once injection procedure is over, take the gun or syringe to pieces, and boil in water for <u>10</u> minutes

- if you inject yourself by accident, seek hospital assistance at once. Take the vial and dilutant with you. You will not die from injecting your finger or hand, but accidental injection does cause blood circulation problems around the injected area

- there are several strains of Mareks disease, but Marexine is the normal vaccine to use

MYCOPLASMA

MYCOPLASMOSIS, CORYZA, COLDS, INFECTIOUS SYNOVITIS, INFECTIOUS SINUSITIS, ROUP

Although all the above diseases are different, they have very similar symptoms and are all treated in the same way.

Classic signs of MYCOPLASMA GALLISEPTICUM, swelling under one or both eyes, often deforming the face of the bird; the smell is awful as well.

SIGNS – Discharge from the nostrils, bubbles in the corner of the eye, scratching the eye area with the foot, wiping infected eye(s) on the base of the neck leaving a tide mark on the feathers, sneezing and rattling often with a noise like 'putark', and an awful smell from the birds' nostrils. As the disease worsens, one or both eyes close with a swelling, (which will harden) under and forward of the eye, which can cause loss of sight in that eye. The bird becomes thinner because of lack of vision. With Infectious synovitis, the hock joints swell, and the bird has difficulty in walking.

CAUSE – An infectious agent called Mycoplasma gallisepticum and Mycoplasma synoviae. This is spread from bird to bird by sneezing, and in the drinking water. This is where auto-drinkers can be a problem. Some birds, if not most, seem to be totally immune. The disease can be transmitted through the egg.

SWOLLEN HOCKS. A very typical sign of MYCLOPLASMA SYNOVITIS.

PREVENTION – Always check the stock that you are buying. The best way is to sniff each bird at the nostrils. If they smell foul, don't buy them. Don't breed from infected stock, and have a good programme of hygiene in place.

TREATMENT – Although you can treat this disease with antibiotics like Terramycin, Tylan Soluble or Aureomycin, it only suppresses the disease which sometimes has an ugly habit of recurring. The Oxytetracyclin drugs are best for Infectious synovitis. I have used Tylan (injectable) 200 into the breast with good results at 1ml for large fowl and ½ml for bantams. It is advisable to cull the badly infected birds,

MORTALITY – Is normally low.

The author checking for MYCOPLASMA. If you sniff the bird's nostrils and the smell is foul, then you can be sure your bird has Mycoplasma

NEWCASTLE DISEASE OR FOWL PEST

You are unlikely to encounter this disease unless there is a national outbreak, which you will hear about anyway. The disease is notifiable which means that, should you think you have the symptoms among your birds, you must contact your local vet or your local MAFF vet immediately.

SIGNS - Are variable, including the necks twisted around, birds flopping about unable to stand, or just twitching. Sometimes there is difficulty in breathing and often a discharge from both ends. Egg production will drop also; there can be high mortality, or only a few birds dying.

CAUSE - There are several strains of this virus, which is part of the Paramyxovirus group. The various viruses will affect all domestic fowl and some wild birds like sparrows and pigeons, so you can see the potential dangers here. The disease attacks the nervous and respiratory systems, hence the lack of co-ordination in the birds. The big worry about the disease is that it can be spread in so many ways, in the wind, physically on boots, crates, feed bags and vehicles, by wild birds and migrating birds and also sometimes in egg form, but this is considered rare.

PREVENTION - If there is cause for alarm, and the disease is in the country and spreading, then you can quite simply vaccinate your flock, be it chickens, ducks, turkeys or pheasants. This treatment is inexpensive, but remember that vaccination is not 100% effective, although it certainly helps. There are two easy ways to vaccinate your flock, either through the drinking water or by spraying your birds with a fine mist so that it is absorbed through the eye.

TREATMENT - There is none, and if your flock becomes infected, there will be a mandatory slaughter programme of all the birds in your area.

MORTALITY - This is of no consequence, because if your birds contract the disease you lose everything anyway. In reality mortality can be low and birds do recover from Newcastle Disease but they are carriers for life having once been infected.

PSITTACOSIS – ORNITHOSIS – CHLAMYDIOSIS

I have put these together because they are all caused by Chlamydia, and I have included it as it appears in the 'What can I catch from my birds?' chapter. It is unlikely that you will come across this, but it can be a problem.

SIGNS – This disease affects mainly young birds as older ones seem to be more resistant to it. Birds show signs of running nostrils and eyes, both very smelly (don't confuse with Mycoplasma). They will be off their food, hunched and cold, with runny or gelatinous droppings, yellowish–green in colour. Egg production plummets.

CAUSE – This is a bacteria called Chlamydia psittaci, which mainly affects pigeons and parrots but is rarely seen in chickens. Transmission is by infected droppings, cuts on the hands, inhaling feather dust, and through crowding birds.

PREVENTION – Providing your house cleaning programme is good and everything is sprayed regularly with a proper disinfectant, there should never be a problem.

TREATMENT – If this does occur and again I stress it is unlikely, check with your vet, and get a good water based broad spectrum antibiotic like Terramycin.

MORTALITY – Low to medium.

THE DIGESTIVE SYSTEM OF A CHICKEN,

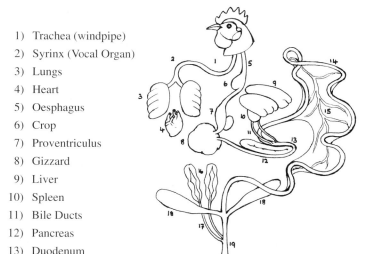

1) Trachea (windpipe)
2) Syrinx (Vocal Organ)
3) Lungs
4) Heart
5) Oesphagus
6) Crop
7) Proventriculus
8) Gizzard
9) Liver
10) Spleen
11) Bile Ducts
12) Pancreas
13) Duodenum

14) Small Intestine
15) Mesentery
16) Kidneys
17) Ureters
18) Caecum
    or Caecal Tracts
19) Rectum
20) Cloaca
    or Vent

Food takes approximately 2½ hours to pass through a chicken

SALMONELLA - Salmonellosis, Pullorum, Fowl typhoid, Fowl paratyphoid

The mention of Salmonella these days causes many people to start worrying about whether eggs or chickens are safe to eat, anxieties which were all stirred up originally by ignorance and the media.

There are hundreds of types of Salmonella bacteria, some more harmful than others, but because a chicken has a high body temperature, most Salmonella are killed off. There are of course exceptions. One of these is Salmonella enteriditis, and this occurs where you find infected foodstuffs, poor hygiene in the food chain, or lack of basic knowledge concerning the storage and cooking of food in the home. The first two factors are becoming less and less of a risk. The other thing to remember is that young children and elderly people have a lower immunity to certain bacteria and should not eat undercooked eggs or food with raw eggs as an ingredient. Back to chickens.

SIGNS - With Salmonella typhimurium, chicks develop pasty or blocked up behinds (vents). They look miserable and cheep all the time, often standing apart from the others. (You rarely see this with chicks under a broody). Salmonella pullorum is mainly seen in adult stock; the birds look unwell, stop laying, and, curiously, have a higher than normal body temperature.

CAUSE - In Salmonella typhimurium and Salmonella pullorum, the bacteria are spread through poor hygiene, stale or infected foodstuffs, dirty nest boxes, rats and mice or wild birds.

PREVENTION - In the case of Salmonella typhimurium, you should always check that the chick crumbs and growers pellets are well within the shelf life time limit: also, regular spraying with Virkon S will stop this disease dead in its tracks. Salmonella pullorum is more difficult to deal with, and here you need to blood test your stock for reactors and carriers. It is rare but it has a habit of cropping up, particularly if you want to export any stock. Testing for Pullorum is difficult; a drop of blood is taken from the vein on the underside of the wing with a small sharp blade, and smeared or dropped on to a special enamel plate. The droplet of blood is then subjected to a droplet of Antigen and the blood either clots or goes runny. If you have a reactor or carrier the blood goes lumpy, and this bird should be culled. The Ministry will test birds for you, or this can be done by your local avian vet.

TREATMENT - Salmonella typhimurium can be cleared up with the probiotic Protexin. Very sick chicks will need to be culled. There are vaccines for Salmonella pullorum but again you would have to check with your vet.

It is interesting to note that no commercial flocks should have Salmonella pullorum as the parent and grandparent stock are rigorously tested for this, so when you are buying your Blackrock, Lohmann Brown, Warren, etc, they should be clear. Quite a few ministry vets consider flocks of hens on smallholdings to be reservoirs for Salmonella pullorum, but in fact this is far from the truth, as nobody is going to keep an unhealthy, non-egg-laying bird.

MORTALITY - Medium.

VENT GLEET

SIGNS - A whitish grey discharge from the vent of the bird; smells nasty. Not to be confused with milky white droppings. This is a discharge that appears to be dribbling all the time, causing the vent area to redden and look very sore.

CAUSE - This is an inflammation in the cloaca, and does not appear to be infectious to other birds. In fact I have seen isolated cases of this complaint several times in batches of otherwise healthy birds.

PREVENTION - There is none.

TREATMENT - The best thign is to cull this bird, but handle it with care, as the discharge is very unpleasant. If the bird is of value to you , a prolonged cleaning up of the vent area with antibiotic solutions might clear up the complaint. (I have never done this so I don't know how effective it is.)

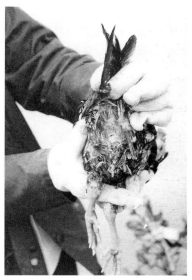

VENT GLEET, a greyish white matter which oozes from the vent.

MORTALITY - In individual birds this is inevitable.

WORMS (Going Light) - Endo-parasites (Endo is Greek for inside)

SIGNS - Loss of weight. Birds appear hungry, sometimes lazy, sometimes there are no signs at all, but loss of weight is apparent when you pick up the bird; the breast bone sticks out like a razor blade. Droppings can be whitish (sometimes confused with Coccidiosis) and as the infestation continues the droppings turn to light green. The birds eventually die.

CAUSE - Internal parasites or worms of which there are many kinds. These fall into three main categories in hens: Large round worms (Ascaridia galli), Hairworm (Capillaria) and Tape worm (Davainea proglottina); all live in the intestines. Two other types of worms are worth mentioning in connection with hens: the Caecal worm (Heterakis gallinarum) which in itself is harmless to hens but carries the protozoan parasite Histomonas meleagridis which causes Blackhead in turkeys and sometimes affects hens, and the Gape worm (Syngamus trachea) which very rarely affects hens but is seen more in partridge and pheasants. If hens are gaping it is more likely to be Avian diphtheria.

PREVENTION - There is no remedy for free range birds. Hens can live with a certain amount of worms in their system and not have a problem, and indeed some hens never seem to be bothered by worms but, like dogs and cats, free range hens should be wormed yearly, and in some cases every six months.

TREATMENT - Flubenvet is the only licensed wormer for poultry and is a very safe drug too. It will kill all the worms found in hens, turkeys, ducks, geese, pheasants, peacocks and guineafowl, but will not affect the parasite Histomonas meleagridis which is spread by the roundworm Heterakis. It is a fine white powder and only a small quantity is needed, about half a teaspoon for six birds each day for seven days. Add a little olive oil or cooking oil to the wheat

This Fayoumi hen died of Worms, (going light). Note the skeletal appearance of the bird with no flesh on

or pellets in a feeding pan, so that the white powder sticks to the food and does not end up uneaten at the bottom of the pan. The 240g tub is designed to mix with 100 kilos of food (ie. 4 sacks of 25 kilos each)

MORTALITY - Medium.

THE DIGESTIVE SYSTEM OF A CHICKEN SHOWING THE AREAS WHERE WORMS THRIVE

1) Oesophagus *(Gullet)*
2) Crop
3) Proventriculus
4) Gizzard
5) Liver
6) Pancreas
7) Duodenum
8) Small Intestine
9) Caecum
   or Caecal Tracts
10) Rectum
11) Cloaca

A) Gape Worm
B) Amidostomum
   (Waterfowl only)
C) Capillaria *(Hairworm)*
D) Acuria *(Roundworm)*
E) Tapeworm
F) Heterakis *(CaecalWorm)*

ALTITUDE

Although this does not apply to England, any poultry kept at high altitudes (4000 metres or above) will be infertile. This is a problem that occurs in Peru and Chile.

BEAK DEFORMITIES

SIGNS - The top mandible is crossed over the lower mandible revealing the tongue of the bird, or the top mandible is arched so the beak cannot close properly. In both cases the bird can have difficulty in eating, but somehow appears to adapt and thrive.

CAUSE - A genetic defect, and poor debeaking

PREVENTION - None.

TREATMENT - In birds that are not too deformed, it is possible to carefully pare the beak back to normal shape, to at least allow the bird to eat and drink, but the beak keeps growing like toenails and will require regular trimming. I nearly always cull these birds because they often look very grotesque.

MORTALITY - As the bird's beak grows so there is more difficulty in feeding and drinking and the bird will eventually die of malnutrition.

DEFORMED BEAKS. Top. Cross beaked. These can be pared down and in time the beak can be made to look fairly normal, but this bird will require attention regularly. Middle. This is more a fault when showing birds. The bird can manage to eat and drink normally, providing the top mandible does not become too arched. Bottom. This bird has suffered from over zealous de-beaking. I have seen many cases like this and in the worst one, the tongue of the bird could be clearly seen. Very often the bird never fully grows the top mandible back to a normal shape.

This bird has an overgrown top mandible, which has prevented it from feeding properly. It looks poor and anaemic, a classic case of a bird whose health has deteriorated due to malnutrtion, and parasites like fleas and lice and mite going into overdrive as well.

BLINDNESS

This is often caused by birds fighting each other or by ammonia or infections like Mycoplasma. The eye goes opaque and the bird tends to tilt her head slightly sideways while feeding and drinking. Some birds live with this for years. There is hereditary blindness in certain breeds, notably Lavender turkeys: the older they get the blinder they become.

BREASTBONE DEFORMITIES

This is seen on birds which have been allowed access to perches too early or where the perches are too narrow. If you run your hand down the breastbone of the bird, you will feel a kink or even an indentation. Resist giving youngstock perches until they are well into their second moult; when this happens will depend on the breed.

If you are rearing on weld mesh wire floors, take care to move your birds onto perches at the right moment (14 - 20 weeks) as you may find the birds' breasts will start to blister.

BUMBLE FOOT

SIGNS - Swelling around the ankle and footpad of the foot, often with lameness.

CAUSE - Often from birds coming down from the perch and landing badly on insufficient and/or wet litter, or from a cut in the foot, both leading to staphylococcal infection.

PREVENTION - Low perches for heavy breeds, higher perches for light breeds, and plenty of litter on the floor of the house to land on.

TREATMENT - Apart from a jab of penicillin, there is little you can do. If the swelling has a head and pus can be removed, so much the better. It is a difficult area to deal with because of all the tendons in the foot, but normally the bird recovers, although the foot remains swollen. This is no good, however, if it is a show bird.

BUMBLE FOOT. A swelling, under or around the ankle joint. Sometimes hard sometimes soft to the touch.

MORTALITY - None unless the infection spreads.

CANNIBALISM

SIGNS - Pecked tails and vents, tips of wings, shoulders and toes. Bleeding and death occurs. Sometimes the insides of the bird are eaten, leaving an empty carcass!

CAUSE - Mainly stress, too much light or bright lighting, overcrowding, lack of food or water, poor quality or stale food, too much disturbance, lack of fresh air, stuffy conditions, low barometric pressure.

PREVENTION - Always use dark heat for young stock still requiring heat. Use either a ceramic bulb or an "electric hen" brooder. Bright heat (i.e. an infra-red or white bulb) never gives the birds any darkness, and young stock need darkness to sleep in: birds grow in their sleep. Another point: infra-red bulbs will degrade the vitamins in chick crumbs if the food is placed near or under them. Great care must be taken during thundery weather as birds can become very restless. Hang up bundles of nettles for them to peck; often they get stung by the nettles and forget about pecking their neighbours. Also, nettles carry insects and are full of iron.

TREATMENT - Remove the badly pecked birds, and either puff them with wound powder and/or spray with gentian violet. Spray any other lightly pecked birds too. The violet changes the raw red wound from red to violet and birds are not attracted to violet as they are to red. Shoulder pecked birds often form a lump on the wing where the muscle has been damaged. These birds are all right for the table but not for stock or showing.

THE SKELETON OF A HEN

1) Upper Mandible
2) Lower Mandible
3) Nasal Passage
4) Forehead
5) Orbital Cavity
6) Occipital
7) Quadratojugal Bone
8) Axis
9) CervicalVertebrae
   (16 of them)
10) DorsalVertebrae
11) Ilium
12) Pelvis
13) Pubic or Pelvic Bones
14) Pygostyle
15) Scapula
16) Coracoide
17) Clavicle (wishbone)
18) Humerus
19) Ulna
20) Radius
21) Carpus
22) Carpus
23) Metacarpus
24) Rudimentary Spur
25) Phalanges

26) Phalanges
27) Phalanges
28) Rib
29) Unicate Process
30) Sternum
31) Ligament Sternum - Clavicle
32) Femur
33) Patella or Rotula
34) Tibia
35) Fibula
36) Metatarsus
37) Metatarsul Spur
38) Basal Phalange
39, 40, 41) Phalanges 2,3,4.

CHOKING OVER FOOD

This happens when birds have been deprived of nourishment and are then given food; they can gorge on it and sometimes choke. If this does happen, just put the food in front of the birds for 20 seconds then remove it for five minutes. Make sure there is adequate drinking water. Repeat this several times until they appear to have eaten enough. Years ago when I was a boy I saw this happen with ducks.

COCK DAMAGE

When breeding from old cocks, there is a chance that the sides of the hens will become lacerated by the cock's spurs during mating. There are two points here: first it is always better from the fertility point of view to use a young bird; second, if you are going to use older cocks, their spurs may need trimming although this may soon be illegal. There are two ways to do this: either hacksaw off the end portion with a fine toothed blade, (this might mean taking off very little as there is a blood vessel running up two thirds of the spur, so approximately a third comes off); then smooth the sharp edges with a nail file. Or with the second method you need to bake 2 small potatoes in the oven until they are soft; impale them on the spurs right up to the leg and leave them on for 5 minutes to soften the horny covering. Then run a sharp knife round the base of the spur and twist off

This old Pekin cock requires some SPUR TRIMMING.

the covering with a pair of pliers. The resulting short stub will make the bird look like a young cockerel! These are the only methods you are allowed to try at home. Spurs can be removed quite easily and quickly by your local vet who cuts off the spur near to the base, and cauterises the blood vessel. For the poor hen with gashes down her sides - take a needle and thread and stitch up the wounds. Don't bunch up the skin too much, and if bleeding occurs puff on some wound powder which will staunch the blood; if it is dry some gentian violet will do the trick. I use a granny knot for the stitches which can be removed after 7 - 10 days. Keep the hen away from cockerels.

CURLY TOES OR CURLY TOE PARALYSIS

SIGNS - At day old the chick has one or both feet with one toe or all the toes bent sideways; the chick moves around but looks ungainly.

CAUSE - There are several factors here. It can be genetic or it can be a vitamin (riboflavin) deficiency in the food, both of which are transmitted through the egg into the embryo. Another factor is the use of bright infra-red bulbs when rearing chicks. Dark heat is preferable in the form of heating elements or gas.

PREVENTION - Curly toes can be passed on from parent stock in two ways. First, check that there are no birds with curly toes in the breeding flock, or a tendency to breed youngstock with curly toes. Secondly, make sure that the foodstuff you buy is the very best and is fresh. Check the sell-by date. It is the vitamin content, particularly riboflavin, which is important, as a lack of this will cause curly toes in chicks. If in doubt, add a little yeast powder, available from your local health food shop, as this is high in riboflavin. The other main factor causing curly toes is the use of bright, particularly white, infra-red bulbs to rear your chicks under. Avoid this and buy a heating element, (dull emitter) which fits in the same porcelain or ceramic holder.

CURLY TOE PARALYSIS. Two badly deformed feet which also caused the loss of a toe.

TREATMENT - Most people in the chicken world cull these chicks but if you have time, or the chick is of a valuable species, it is possible to correct this fault. As soon as the chick is hatched, take a length of sticky tape, make a loop with the sticky side upwards and turn the ends under to stick on the table: place the chick's foot on the sticky tape with the toe nails sticking out but the toes in the spread position. With another length of sticky tape, make a sandwich of the toes and press the tape round them to hold them in place, and then trim with scissors. Cut off the original bits which were secured to the table. Leave the tape on for a week then remove it and clean up the toes and feet.

MORTALITY - Normally zero except for culling.

EAR INFECTION

SIGNS - The bird is unbalanced and appears to be listening very hard; obviously rather hard of hearing - one or both ears blocked with yellowish matter.

CAUSE - Local infection in the ear, probably caused by a seed or some other irritant.

PREVENTION - There is none.

TREATMENT - Using the round end of a small lady's hair grip, or a paper clip, clean out the yellowish matter as carefully as possible, (it is sometimes evil smelling). A pair of tweezers is useful too, and sometimes the matter will come out like a carrot. The bird needs a jab of antibiotic or penicillin.

MORTALITY - None unless the infection spreads.

EGGS

BLOOD ON EGG - Very often this is seen on pullet eggs, the first ones the bird produces. There are red streaks along the egg from where the oviduct has had to expand to allow it to pass. Normally this clears up leaving clean eggs.

BLOOD SPOTS ON EGGS - The eggs are covered with several small red blood spots, caused by an infestation of red mite. This means that your birds are hopping with parasites, so the house needs cleaning and spraying and the birds need to be dusted with flea/lice powder.

MIS-SHAPEN EGGS - The main cause for this is stress or some challenge to the birds' normal life style. Birds that are too fat will lay mis-shapen eggs, as will birds that suffer from Infectious Bronchitis.

SOFT SHELLED EGGS - Most birds produce several soft shelled eggs when they come into lay. These are often found under the perches, just a residue

A pullet's first egg, soft shelled, and often quite round, as compared with an egg from the same bird a week later.

of skin, others are found entire in the nest box, like soft pingpong balls. Normally the bird grows out of laying soft shelled eggs, but some persist. It is vitally important that your birds have access to mixed grit at all times, to be able to take up the calcium to form the egg shells. Some hens do have a malfunctioning oviduct and will always lay soft and/or irregular shaped eggs.

EGG BOUND

Not many people realise that this is cramp, the muscles around the vent area seizing up and not allowing the egg to pass. The poor hen is crouched straining away and sometimes the egg is just visible. You can dab some olive oil around the vent area, but what the bird really wants is warmth. There are several ways of helping the egg to pass: you can give the hen an enema of liquid paraffin or olive oil, or if she is quiet, warm up the vent area with a hair drier. Another way is to place the bird on some straw or shavings in a cardboard box with ventilation holes and then put the box and bird on a radiator or Aga. The egg will pass after a few hours. It may not be a double yolker but it is wise to ring the bird in case this happens again.

EGG EATING

If egg eating was discovered in past times, all sorts of concoctions were used, such as mustard, chilli and curry, to try to stop this vice, but once it has started it is very difficult to clear up. The reasons for egg eating are legion: boredom, poorly constructed nest boxes, lack of nest boxes, lack of litter in the nest boxes, nest boxes too tight, lack of grit, poor diet, to name a few. The best remedy is to put plastic bits in the hens' beaks and this usually stops egg eating and feather pecking immediately. While the bits are in you must feed pelleted food and/or whole wheat, and <u>not</u> mash as the birds cannot take it up.

Bits to prevent feather pulling and egg eating

FEATHER PECKING

This is a vice which is sometimes difficult to stop, and can be seen in birds of all ages. This section should be read in conjunction with Cannibalism and Moulting.

SIGNS - Loss of feathers around the head, neck, back and bottom.

<u>FEATHER LOSS ON THE HEAD, WINGS & BACK:</u> - This is mainly due to the cockerel causing damage during the act of mating. Some hens are not badly affected, others look badly mauled. The main damage is on the back, and the cockerel hangs on to the hen's head with his beak to steady himself, hence the loss of feathers to the head. Saddles made of canvas were used in the old days to prevent back damage. Feather loss is more noticeable in soft feather breeds like Sussex, Orpington, Maran, etc.

<u>FEATHER LOSS ON THE NECK:</u> - There are two main causes of feather loss on the neck:

1) Northern Fowl Mite. This is a persistent external parasite. See Northern Fowl Mite. Hens scratch out their neck feathers because of this irritation.

2) If a hen run becomes denuded of vegetation, the hens will very often push their heads through the wire mesh to get to fresh grass etc. There is often feather loss to the neck caused by this action.

FEATHER LOSS ON THE BOTTOM: Mainly seen on laying hens, and the skin often looks red. This can be a combination of a good laying bird, sometimes with fleas, lice and mites towards the end of its egg laying life before a moult. Apart from dusting the birds with flea powder there is nothing much you can do. In severe cases the bird will strip itself of feathers, making large areas completely bald. This is stress related. I have seen it in battery caged birds and parrots.

FEATHER DAMAGE: - This is a peculiar problem, but one of management more than anything. It happens mainly to caged birds, and you will find that suddenly the ends of the tail or other feathers appear to have been snipped off during the night. The answer is mice!

FLEAS & LICE (Ecto-parasites) Ecto is Greek for outside

SIGNS - Without inspecting your hens closely there are usually few traces of fleas to be seen except for the birds scratching and pecking themselves which they do normally anyway. But in bad cases, the birds will show signs of being unwell, will stop laying, or get up off eggs in the case of a broody hen. Often the face becomes pale and shrunk and the bird looks miserable. In cock birds there will be reduced fertility. Closer inspection will reveal a bird with an array of creepy-crawlies (fleas and lice) and very often white clusters on the base of the feathers around the vent area. These are the eggs of the lice.

Polands as a breed suffer from FLEAS and LICE in their crests. Too often one sees semi-bald heads, the result of the birds scratching their crests, Regular checking and applications of flea powder are essential.

CAUSE - Fleas can jump. Lice are wingless. Fleas will sometimes lay eggs on the bird in the nest box or on the floor of the hen house. Lice always lay on the bird, normally in white clusters around the vent area. Fleas are narrow and colourless and suck blood from the bird via the base of the feather. Lice are flat, yellow and tough, and mainly live off feathers and skin debris. Blood sucking by fleas can cause anaemia and death, hence the pale shrivelled look in birds badly infested. Fleas and lice come in from wild birds, and warm weather

Typical of an infestation of LICE; white clusters of eggs around the vent area, adhering to the base of the feathers.

28

seems to increase infestations. There are four types of chicken louse, the most common being the Yellow Body Louse.

PREVENTION - Check your birds by hand and eye as regularly as possible for signs of infestation, and have a routine delousing programme.

TREATMENT - Most people use a pyrethrum based powder which works very well. Hold the bird on your lap on some newspaper and inspect the vent area. If there are any clusters of lice eggs pull out the affected feathers with a swift movement. Turn the bird over and hold her down with one hand while you puff or sprinkle the flea powder liberally round the vent area, under the wings, on the neck and breast then over and along the back. Rub the powder well in - the fleas and lice will be dead in no time.

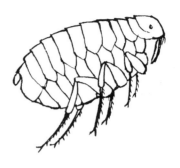

Hen Flea ECHIDNOPHAGA GALLINACEA.

A new, and as yet unlicensed method of de-lousing your birds is to use Front-Line (Rhone-Merieux) Spot On for dogs. The solution is dripped on to the bird's neck and spreads around the whole body within 24 hours. Any fleas or lice will be dead within 24/48 hours. The treatment is effective for 2 months in dogs, and incidentally, has been used on falcons.

MORTALITY - Low.

DE-FLEAING BIRDS. Sit down with some newspaper on your lap. Turn the bird onto its back, and rub flea powder into the feathers, holding the bird firmly by the legs. Make sure special attention is paid to the vent, breast, back and neck areas. Repeat after 7 days if the infestation is bad.

FOX-BITES

Very often after a raid by foxes, one or two birds escape but with bites to their bodies. Providing the teeth have not punctured any main organs and the wound is a flesh bite, the bird will survive, even though it will have been terribly traumatised. It is best to have it injected with penicillin by your local vet as foxes carry harmful bacteria in their mouths, mainly from eating carrion.

FROSTBITE

This is rare in most parts of England but the further north you go, the more the possibility arises. I did see evidence of this when we had a severe winter in the early

1970's. One case was a guinea fowl that lost all its toes; they went black and turned into 'twigs' finally breaking off and leaving the bird with three stumps on which it managed perfectly well for many years! The other case was a Light Sussex cock which lost all the points of its comb. These again went black and fell off one by one, leaving a relatively smooth comb - this is why most of the breeds in America have rosecombs, to avoid this problem. Obviously if you are in an area where the temperature falls sharply, you must consider insulation and heating for your birds.

When I was in Russia it was interesting to see that most of the poultry keepers either kept their birds in their flats, or in heated garages because the winters there are so fierce.

 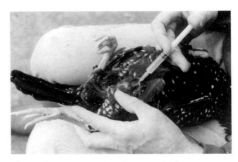

Two locations for injections in young or adult birds, either in the breast or the thigh. If the bird is very thin, injecting in the thigh is best.

HEART PROBLEMS

SIGNS - Mauve or deep red comb; the bird panting or short of breath. The bird is often slightly over-weight, and symptoms appear when it is being caught. This occurs mainly in older birds and cockerels.

CAUSES - Enlarged or defective heart. I would suggest not to breed from this bird as it could be a genetic condition.

PREVENTION - If the bird is special, try to make sure it is not stressed. Birds with this condition live for a year or so, providing they have a quiet life.

TREATMENT - There is none.

MORTALITY - High.

NORTHERN FOWL MITE

SIGNS - Mainly seen as dirty feathers on white or buff birds; this is the excrement of the mite. Birds look as though they have had a dirty dust bath.

CAUSE - The Northern Fowl Mite's Latin name is Ornythonyssus sylviarum. This mite differs from red mite in that it lives on the bird full time and has a seven day life cycle.

PREVENTION - Regular cleaning and disinfection of the house.

TREATMENT - If only a few birds are involved, it is best to wash them in a bucket of warm water with Dettol or another gentle disinfectant. (Jeyes is for lavatories!) Dunk the bird in and splash as much as you can around the head. Get the bird thoroughly soaked. Dry it off with a towel first, and then a hair dryer, until the feathers are dry, and always return the birds to a disinfected house. Northern Fowl Mite is very persistent, and if you use pyrethrum powder, you must do so every 8 days for two weeks.

MORTALITY - Low.

RED MITE (White mite are young red mite)

SIGNS - None or rarely on the birds. Birds can look off colour and pale in the face (anaemic). Red clusters around the perch sockets and on the roof and walls of the house. The young mite are whitish in colour and make your head itch if they get in your hair! They are mostly seen during periods of warm weather but can appear at any time.

CAUSE - Dermanyssus gallinae is the villain. It spends only part of its time on the bird, mainly at night sucking blood, hence the red clusters; if you squash them you will have blood on your hands. The rest of the time it lives and lays its eggs in the crevices, cracks, or tongue and groove of the poultry house, and it thrives between the timber and the felt on the roof. The life cycle of the red mite is 7 - 10 days.

A perch socket showing typical signs of RED MITE, pieces of quill follicles, and clumps of red mite. They do not like bright light so hide themselves during the day in any crevices they can find.

PREVENTION - Regular cleaning and disinfection of the houses

TREATMENT - Clean out the house; take it apart if sectional and spray it with Duramitex. If you have a felt roof on the house, rip it off: felt roofs on chicken houses are a disaster. Allow it to dry, and reassemble it. Do this again the following week to catch the newly hatched mites.

MORTALITY - It does happen with poor management, but is uncommon.

MOULTING & FEATHER GROWING PATTERNS

There are three things that tell us that hens have developed from reptiles: the beak and skull, the scales on the legs, and the way that hens will hiss at you like a snake if you disturb them on eggs. Then there is a fourth clue and that is the way they change their feathers. Just as a snake sloughs its skin annually, so also do the hen and cock lose their feathers each year.

The signs of moulting are feather loss and egg laying coming to an end; sometimes the feathers come out gradually, sometimes they seem to drop off like leaves after a frost.

When the chick is hatched it is covered with down which looks more like hair. These hairs grow from tiny capsules which cover the chick's body. During the first week quills, pens and sheaths appear on the wings and the first feathers come through. After 4-6 weeks the young bird has nearly all its first feathers, but this can depend on the breed. Some are very quick to feather up such as light breeds like Leghorns and Anconas, and some are slower such as heavier breeds like Speckled Sussex or Buff Orpington.

At approximately 14-22 weeks, again depending on the breed, the bird changes its feathers once more for its adult ones. All the wing feathers drop and the new ones start pushing through from the centre of the wing. The tail feathers grow, defining male and female; in the case of the female this is called a Pullet Tail, and when it is completely formed the bird will start to lay providing there is enough daylight.

Now this is where there is a hitch in the process. The annual moult in older birds takes place as the days become shorter, (August, September, October or November), and takes 2-3 months to complete. If, however, our January/February hatched pullet comes into lay in July or August it can lay a few eggs and then, as if getting into rhythm, moult again. This can be overcome by artificial lighting in the house. Sometimes these pullets will lay satisfactorily and come mid-winter will have a neck-moult, just involving the feathers round the head and neck. Again, egg production stops, but this is only a quick moult and the bird will be back in lay after about four weeks.

Look out for the birds which lose the most feathers: they are the best layers, and the birds which hold their feathers are poorer layers. Older birds will hold their feathers more as well. Some exhibition stock come into this category because their owners want their birds to look their best for as long as possible, and consequently the birds are poor layers.

You will notice that when the feathers fall out, the bird becomes covered with pin feathers (undeveloped feathers) and can sometimes look like a hedgehog. At this stage it needs vitamin and mineral supplements added to its food, and a little minced dog or cat food does not go amiss either.

If birds are stressed they will often go into a moult. This can happen for a wide variety of reasons: if there is a sudden change in foodstuffs; if drinking water is forgotten and the birds become thirsty; if they are shut up in a hot henhouse; or if they are being transported in hot weather ; in fact, anything which is severely out of the ordinary. In the old days artificial moults were induced in order to have birds laying at a certain time. This is still practised on certain commercial farms and is mainly achieved with lighting and/or withdrawal of food.

Clipping feathers around the vent area to facilitate mating. Mainly done in more 'fluffy' breeds like Pekins, Orpingtons, Cochins and Brahmas.

There is an exception to this moulting process; in Japan there is a breed called the o-naga-dori, o=tail, naga=long, dori=fowl: the long tailed fowl. This moults everything except its tail feathers which grow progressively longer every year. There aren't very many of these birds , probably about 60. They are a status symbol, and their tails can grow to over 10 metres or 30 feet long.

As a matter of interest the average hen carries between 8,500-9,000 feathers.

NUTRITIONAL DISORDERS

In the old days when people fed their birds on scraps from the kitchen there was sometimes a problem with an unbalanced diet, but nutritional disorders are now a thing of the past as we can buy poultry food already made up as a balanced diet and vitamin supplements to go with it. Having said that however, some of these foodstuffs are less than ideal as they still contain ingredients such as egg colourants, coccidiostats, and waste by-products from the food industry, and there is a move to make hens more and more vegetarian with the clean up of the animal feed business resulting from the B.S.E. scare. Hens are actually omnivores and some of the new rations are lacking the vital protein factor. If you ever see a mouse in a poultry house, the hens are as eager as terriers to catch it and eat it! I find that a small tin of the fishy dog or cat food once a month doesn't go amiss, although legally this is unacceptable.

POISON

Most poisoning cases in poultry occur from two sources: rat poison and aflatoxin poisoning from foodstuffs. Years ago before I invented the DFR rat box, I saw what happened when some hens accidentally gained access to rat poison. They appeared off colour and bled from the vent, ear and beak. Some recovered, but I had to cull several.

Aflatoxin poisoning can happen when food, particularly grains like maize, has been stored in a damp place. The toxin comes from a fungus called Aspergillis flavus that grows on the grain. It is not common but is something you should be aware of.

Some people think that if they allow their birds into the garden they will be poisoned by the various plants growing there. In reality this does not usually happen, as most poisonous plants are bitter to the taste, but it could occur with young inexperienced birds. Most people know the poisonous plants in their gardens, and here are the names of a few common ones: Yew, Privet, Laburnum, Aconitum napellus (Monk's Hood), Euphorbia, Lords and Ladies (Avum), Datura and Foxglove. It is the alkaloids in these plants which are poisonous, but the interesting point here is that some of these plants are used in medicine, in a more dilute form. Ivy is not poisonous. I know this as I have a young cockerel running around the house (for research purposes), and he demolished an ivy plant without ill effect.

PROLAPSE

This is not often seen but does happen quite unexpectedly sometimes.

SIGNS - The first sign of this is a bird with its oviduct protruding out of the vent in a red mass with the other birds in the pen taking a keen interest, often pecking at the red protuberance, which will lead to the death of the bird. Quite often the other hens will peck the afflicted bird clean of all its innards.

CAUSE - There are several causes: young birds coming into lay too early, a bird passing a too large or irregular egg; birds that are overweight or fat will prolapse, also birds with a defect of the oviduct.

PREVENTION - The only situation where a remedy is possible is where birds are artificially induced to lay too soon by means of additional lighting. Decrease the lighting and allow the birds to come into lay naturally.

TREATMENT - I have tried several ways and several times to save a bird in this situation, but the problem lies with the area which is very complex. The bird not only passes eggs through the vent but also faeces (droppings). I have tried gently pushing the oviduct back into the vent which it seems to accept, although I have been conscious of the action of bacteria and sunlight on this organ. I have even tried to stitch the oviduct in, but I am afraid to no avail. I believe the muscle walls are weakened by this and never seem to recover. Sadly there is nothing one can do except for veterinary surgery.

RINGS

Too often I have seen rings which are either too loose or too tight on a bird's leg. Particular care should be taken when colour ringing youngstock through to adulthood, as you may re-quire as many as five different sizes to ensure that the bird is not put at any risk. The alternative to rings is wing tags. These can be put on at day old and sit comfortably under the bird's wing. The only disadvantage is that you cannot always identify your bird without first picking it up.

This shows a problem with a ring that was too large for the leg, and the bird tried to scratch it off. The ring should fit snugly on the leg, above the spur.

ROACH BACK

Mainly seen in young cockerels, where the back appears to be lopsided. If you run your hand down the bird's back you may find a lump on one side just below the wings and above the tail. There isn't much you can do, apart from fatten the bird up or cull it. It is not known if this complaint is hereditary.

A classic case of WRYE TAIL. Very often the bird will be ROACH BACKED as well.

SCALEY - LEG

SIGNS - Scales lifted on the leg, lameness, toes and legs looking as though they are encrusted with white flaky matter. It appears to be more common in feather legged breeds, such as Silkies, Pekins or Faverolles.

CAUSE - Scaley leg is caused by a mite called Cnemido-coptes mutans which lives under the scales. The leg swells because of fluid production caused by the irritation of the mite.

PREVENTION - Regular cleaning and disinfecting of the house and perches.

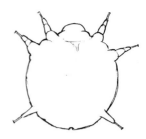

SARCOPTES MUTANS or SCALEY LEG MITE. (Greatly magnified)

TREATMENT - In the old days people used paraffin and even creosote. If you have ever got creosote in a cut on your hand you will know how painful it is. Today, although there are potions and aerosols on the market, the best way to clear up Scaley Leg is with surgical spirit. Fill a wide necked jar with surgical spirit, clean the leg of any dirt and dunk it in, up to the hock joint. Hold the leg in for 20 seconds. The bird will flinch a bit because the liquid is cold. Do the other leg then repeat this four more times at weekly intervals. Take care not to pick the scales off the leg as it will bleed easily. You may also find that the bird might lose a toe, or part of a toe. The leg will take anything up to a year to heal.

MORTALITY - Low.

A very bad case of SCALEY LEGS. In such cases a bird will often lose a toe or part of a foot.

SEX CHANGE

SIGNS - This occurs in adult birds from female to male. The bird starts to crow and grow a longer tail. Gradually the bird looks more and more like a male bird and it obviously does not lay. This sex change sometimes lasts only a season or a year, but can go on for longer.

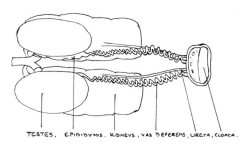

TESTES, EPIDIDYMIS, KIDNEYS, VAS DEFERENS, URETA, CLOACA.

Cock's reproductive System

CAUSE - There seem to be two main reasons for this (a) Genetic - If the bird is carrying more male genes, it will change sex if given the opportunity, such as in an all female flock of birds or if a dominant cockerel is removed (b) Damage caused by fighting, injury or stress. The reproductive organs can be affected causing a temporary or total change of sex.

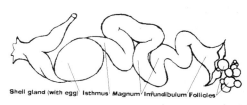

Shell gland (with egg) Isthmus Magnum Infundibulum Follicles

Hen's reproductive system

SOUR CROP (Candidiasis or Moniliasis) and IMPACTED CROP

SIGNS - A bulging crop: in the case of Sour Crop, a soft enlarged crop, and in the case of Impacted Crop, it is hard. N.B. birds often go to roost with a bulging crop. In old hens Sour Crop makes the crop rather pendulous. Mainly seen in hens rather than cockerels. Birds will sometimes be seen eating mud to try to alleviate it.

CAUSE - Sour Crop is caused by a fungus called Candida albicans developing inside and causing the crop to enlarge and fill with evil-smelling liquid. Impacted Crop is caused by too much fibre intake (grass, straw, hay) in young birds. The crop becomes rock hard, thus preventing any food, or little food from passing through.

Administering natural yogurt to a bird with SOUR CROP

PREVENTION - Sour Crop. Little is known as to why or how the bird picks up the fungus so there is not much you can do to prevent it. It may be caused by stress. Impacted Crop normally happens when birds are moved from one rearing system to another, i.e. from a wire mesh floor to a floor with straw or grass. The new surroundings can cause the birds to gorge themselves, resulting in the crop impaction. Rake up any new mown grass clippings and make sure there are enough feeders and drinkers in the new area.

TREATMENT - Both complaints are treated with natural live yoghurt. In the case of Sour Crop, try to make the bird vomit as much as possible by holding its head down and kneading with your hand until the crop is empty. It is a foul job! Once most of the crop is empty, feed the bird liquid live yoghurt with the aid of a plastic syringe. Do this a couple of times a day for two days. The yoghurt acts as a probiotic and sorts out the fungus, and normally all is well. Do the same with crop impaction, although obviously you can't make the bird sick. The results with crop impaction are not quite as good.

MORTALITY - Medium.

STRESS

This is one of the main problems when keeping poultry from day old to adult, and is a subject rarely mentioned in poultry books. As I have written elsewhere, stress lowers the immune system, allowing other problems to come in and take over. Stress can be triggered in many ways, for example, by heat or cold, noise and disturbance, change of food, lack of food and water, transport, new surroundings, or introduction to new birds.

Hens have a high metabolic rate which makes their nervous systems very acute, giving rise to a high stress level. Curiously they can be very tolerant of chronic stress, as seen in battery cage birds.

Stress is very difficult to measure, but we do see outward and visible signs such as shoulder or vent pecking, panting, cannibalism, watery diarrhoea, head flicking in caged birds, and moulting.

In the old days, the poultry keeper really only had Tincture of Iodine (1 teaspoonful per gallon of water) to help his/her birds along. Fortunately nowadays we have Probiotics. These can be administered in the water or the food, and at any age. The advantages of Probiotics are as follows:

a) They help to promote growth in a natural way

b) They protect birds from harmful forms of E-Coli and bacteria

c) They help the immune system by boosting interferon production

d) They protect hens from Salmonella including Typhimurium and Interiditis

e) They help protect birds against certain cancers

So all in all a useful tool, should you need it.

When to use Probiotics? I have used it very successfully on day old and young chicks through to growers. I remember one case at the Food and Farming Festival at Hyde Park where there were some young chicks under a bright infra-red bulb, pecking each other to death. They had become very stressed by the hot weather, the infra-red bulb and the constant handling by children. The owners were very worried and asked for help. I put a couple of teaspoonfuls of Protexin in the chicks' water and within a few hours they were back to normal. It is also not a bad idea to put some Protexin in the water of exhibition birds once they are back from shows which can cause birds a lot of stress; you can see this if you weigh them before and after.

So what is this magic compound? It is a kind of dried yoghurt which contains beneficial micro-organisms which rearrange the flora, or naturally occurring bacteria, in the intestines. The benefits of yoghurt have been recognised for years, particularly in India, where the food can be hot and spicy; very often you are given yoghurt after the meal, or a yoghurt drink called 'Lassie' during the meal, to help digest your food.

Treatment with Protexin Probiotics should be as follows:

5g or 1 teaspoon per ½ gallon of water for the soluble kind of Protexin or 5g or 1 teaspoon per 5 lbs or 2.2 kilos of food for the infeed Protexin.

For the first week of life chicks should be given soluble Protexin only. As soon as each chick has hatched, dip its beak in the soluble Protexin solution.

SUFFOCATION

A rarely mentioned problem.

SIGNS - Dead birds in corners, some-times piled up on top of each other, some looking quite naked.

A typical situation with young pullets, often leading to suffocation.

CAUSE - Power cuts, the heat source is lost and birds huddle to keep warm; moving birds from one house to another; moving birds from a bright heat source to a dark house at night; using solid floors instead of slatted or weld mesh floors in night houses; poor ventilation; birds either too hot or to cold at night.

39

PREVENTION - Be careful about moving birds from one type of housing to another. Be sure that they are the right age to move, have feathered up sufficiently, and that the new house is warm enough and has adequate ventilation. Make sure that the floor has slats or weld mesh narrow enough so the birds don't get their heads or legs stuck, and block off the corners with weld mesh. The idea is that when the birds huddle together at night the middle birds are not suffocated, but can breathe either by raising or lowering their heads.

TREATMENT - Sometimes the odd bird can be found alive, but they nearly always die, probably because of oxygen starvation to the brain.

MORTALITY - Can be high.

TOE BALLS

I have put this complaint in as it is a problem that occurs when young birds are not cleaned out regularly. Droppings etc from the straw, shavings or litter, ball up under the feet and particularly around the nails. These harden and increase in size, until they are sometimes as big as a pea. If they are not dealt with, the young birds may risk losing their toe nail and/or the end section or digit of the toe. If the balls are small, gently unpick them, pulling away and down from the toe. If they are large, take some kitchen scissors and snip off the worst; be careful of the toe nail inside. Then

TOE BALLS

soak the bird's feet in warm water, and the balls of muck will gradually soften. This is a salutary lesson; never be slack about your cleaning routine.

WATERBELLY

This is a complaint found mainly in older birds, where large blisters or sacks of fluid appear between the legs and up the breast bone. It seems as though it is caused by mal-absorption of water but because it occurs in old birds, it has never been properly investigated. The bird should be culled. This complaint is rare, and may possibly be caused by trauma.

WING CLIPPING - Cutting the primary feathers with scissors on one wing only. See Ducks and Geese section WING CLIPPING

WOODSHAVINGS

Just a word about this as certain woodshavings are toxic, particularly those from timber which has been treated, and certain hardwoods, (Iroka from West Africa is one) so if a friend offers you woodshavings from his workshop, be careful. All woodshavings sold at petshops and agricultural merchants are perfectly safe to use.

DUCKS AND GEESE

Waterfowl keepers are lucky as ducks and geese kept on a free range basis are subject to very few diseases, but they do have their fair share of problems.

B =	CAUSED BY A BACTERIA	C =	CHICK 1-3 weeks
V =	CAUSED BY A VIRUS	G =	GROWER 4-12 weeks
F =	CAUSED BY A FUNGUS	A =	ADULT 13+ weeks

DISEASE	TYPE OF DISEASE	AGE OF SUSCEPTIBILITY			PAGE
Aspergillosis	F		C	G A	43
Avian tuberculosis	B	A			43
Botulism	B		C	G A	44
Duck virus enteritis	V			G A	44
E-Coli	B		C	G A	45
Newcastle Disease	V		C	G A	45
Pasteurellosis	B		C	G A	45
Worms	P			G A	46

Problems encountered in Ducks and Geese:

	Page		Page
Blindness	47	Lead Poisoning	49
Corns	47	Moult	49
Dirty or Sticky Eye	47	Obstructions	49
Dropped Tongue	48	Penis Paralysis	50
Lameness	49	Prolapse	50

	Page			Page
Protruding Sinus	51	Stress (Off Legs)		54
Sex Change	51	Wet Feather		54
Slipped Tendon in Leg	52	Wing Clipping /		
Slipped Wing (Angel Wings)	52	Permanent Pinioning		54
Staggers / Sunstroke	53	General		55

MORTALITY: Is expressed as the number of birds in your flock which are likely to die from the disorder. LOW is 10% and less, MEDIUM is 50% and less, HIGH is 50% and above.

ASPERGILLOSIS - This is a disease caused by slack management.

SIGNS - This disease is seen in young birds reared artifically on dirty and wet straw, hay or sawdust. Aspergillosis is normally associated with wet and mouldy hay. The young birds are heard gasping and gaping for air, and die quickly.

CAUSE - A fungus called Aspergillosis fumigatus which is present everywhere, especially in warm damp conditions. It is particularly prevalent with ducklings and goslings reared on straw or shavings because they splash their water around so much.

PREVENTION - If possible, rear young waterfowl on wire mesh with a droppings tray underneath. If this is not possible, clean out the straw or sawdust on a daily basis, so that the fungus does not have a chance to develop. Disinfect with Virkon S regularly.

TREATMENT - There is none, apart from the above.

MORTALITY - Low to medium.

AVIAN TUBERCULOSIS

SIGNS - The odd bird showing signs of unthriftyness, lameness, some diarrhoea, obviously thin and hungry, in fact all the signs of worms. Normally seen in older birds, as the disease is chronic. Have this bird post-mortemed.

CAUSE - Is the Mycobacterium avium, which is spread by contact with infected birds or soil, on hands, feet, crates, housing and wild birds. It can remain in the soil for up to five years.

PREVENTION - Be careful about buying breeding stock of more than two years old. Blood tests can now check if your birds are infected. Further details from your vet.

TREATMENT - There is none.

There are two points I would like to make here. First, although Avian T.B. can in theory be spread through the egg, this is highly unlikely. Second, Mycobacterium avium is different from T.B. in man, but those handling a lot of T.B. infected birds might well react to a human T.B. test.

MORTALITY - Low.

BOTULISM

Rarely seen.

SIGNS - Birds dying very quickly, often with their necks and heads stretched over their backs.

CAUSE - Dirty and stagnant water, coupled with hot weather. A strong toxin is produced by the bacterium Clostridium botulinum which is attracted to decomposing carcases such as dead rats, and is thus picked up by the bird.

PREVENTION - Fence off ponds that become stagnant and foul in summer, and use clean tap water in basins or troughs. Move the birds to clean ground.

TREATMENT - There is an anti-toxin to Clostridium botulinum; check with your vet, but the best thing is to avoid this situation in the first place.

MORTALITY - High.

DUCK VIRUS ENTERITIS or Duck Plague

SIGNS - Ducks showing signs of being off colour one day and dead the next. They tend to sit about, eyes half closed and sometimes with heads moving about. It can affect all ages, but is mainly seen in young stock. The birds appear to be in good condition, which makes this disease all the more annoying. Brown or green faeces. Muscovies can be prone to this.

CAUSE - A contagious virus which affects the blood causing it to clot, with haemorrhages in the main organs as well. There is certainly a connection with wild mallard, which are known carriers. The disease appears to be water borne, and is encountered where ducks are kept too crowded and in dirty conditions.

PREVENTION - Move the birds to fresh ground; keep them away from dirty water, and use plastic or fibre-glass ponds with clean water. Wash and disinfect all equipment involved with these birds. Try to limit contact with wild mallard.

TREATMENT - Terramycin in the water for seven days.

MORTALITY - High.

E-COLI

This is not a common disease, but will be found if conditions are less than adequate.

SIGNS - Mainly seen in young ducks between 2-9 weeks of age; ducks look 'tucked up' with their heads into their bodies, and in severe cases die rapidly. In many ways this disease looks like Pasteurellosis.

CAUSE - E-Coli makes ducks feel off-colour and E-Coli with septicaemia causes their death. The disease is spread by infected droppings and dirty egg shells.

PREVENTION - Use good husbandry, a proper cleaning schedule, and reduce the number of birds in that area. Ensure that clean water is available.

TREATMENT - A broad spectrum antibiotic like Terramycin in the water will normally clear this up. Remove birds from the contaminated area.

MORTALITY - Low to medium.

NEWCASTLE DISEASE

It is worth mentioning that ducks are susceptible to Newcastle Disease, but another virus within the same disease. There are different types of Newcastle Disease (Paramyxovirus) for different species. One affects pigeons, another budgerigars etc. but unfortunately these types sometimes cross over, and can also be spread by wild birds; it is very rare in waterfowl however. For symptoms see Hens and Bantams.

PASTEURELLOSIS OR DUCK CHOLERA

SIGNS - This affects both young and old. The symptoms are very similar to E-Coli, birds being 'tucked up' and necks drawn into their bodies, but with more deaths.

CAUSE - Is a bacteria called Pasteurella multocida. The disease is carried in by wild birds, vermin, or water, and on people and in food. It can also be introduced by a carrier bird. It is very contagious.

PREVENTION - As with E-Coli, good husbandry and a good hygiene programme are essential; reduce the levels of stock and ensure that the water available is clean, and also the pasture.

TREATMENT - With large numbers of dead birds on your hands you will need to call in the local specialist vet. It is possible to treat this with antibiotics, but if your ducks have this disease, there is something radically wrong with the way you are keeping them.

MORTALITY - Medium to high.

WORMS

This is one of the most troublesome problems when keeping ducks and geese. I say this, as most people who have a collection of waterfowl have regular problems with worms. However, some people never have to worm their birds at all or so they tell me!

SIGNS - Limping is one of the first signs of worms, together with loss of condition and feathers looking dull. Catch the bird, examine it, and check its weight; can you easily feel the breast bone? Birds in an advanced stage of worms can be seen to be gaping, very light in weight, and listless, the head appearing too big for the body. Young birds: sleepy looking, not interested in food, or perhaps ravenously hungry. Very often whitish and runny droppings, turning green in later stages. The bird dies of Peritonitis, blood poisoning.

CAUSE - Ducks and geese have their own set of worms which differ from those of hens and bantams.

Cyathostoma bronchialis. This is a worm that infects the windpipe and the top of the lungs.

Amidostomum anseris, or gizzard worm, mainly found in geese.

Echimuria unginata or Acuariasis, mainly in ducks: a roundworm which infects the glands of the stomach. This is spread by the water flea Daphnia.

Tapeworms and Flatworms: although ducks and geese sometimes carry these worms, they are not normally a problem.

PREVENTION - Worm all new stock coming in, reduce stocking densities, alternate paddocks or runs, provide clean drinking and swimming water.

TREATMENT - Luckily Flubenvet (it used to be called Mebenvet) is a very effective drug for clearing up worms. It not only kills the worms but is also very effective against their eggs. Try to worm your birds in an area that you can clean up like a concrete yard, or on wire mesh, or in an area of the garden the birds don't normally have access to. It is a question of trying to stop the cycle of worm infestation. Flubenvet is a very safe drug. It is like fine white flour and to ensure that your birds take it up, mix it with your grain/pellets in a container and add a little olive or cooking oil so that the powder sticks to the food. Do this for seven days.

Quantities: If you have only a few birds (4-6) about ¼ - ½ a teaspoon per feed. It does not have to be precise as the drug is very safe. Don't eat the eggs during worming, as a precaution. I have found that dead worms start to pour out about day 4 in badly infected birds; the size of the worm burdens can sometimes be really quite alarming.

MORTALITY - Medium.

BLINDNESS

Obviously this can occur from physical damage, fighting etc, but it is also seen in certain breeds that have been bred very closely, particularly Call ducks and Indian Runner ducks. The young birds appear to be healthy, but after a year or eighteen months a white spot appears on the iris of the eye. Sometimes it is only one eye, and then it progresses to both. There is nothing to do but cull the bird.

CORNS

SIGNS - Bird limping, the foot obviously showing signs of being painful. Pick the bird up and look on the under part of the foot. There may be one or more wart-like sores to be seen.

CAUSES - This is a local infection (possibly staphylococcal) which has taken hold in a crack of the foot and has enlarged.

CORNS. A very common complaint in ducks and geese, in summer time. Note the fly.

PREVENTION - This problem normally occurs in summer when the ground is hard, or where the birds have to cross an unmade road or concrete on their way to feed or water. Lack of swimming water can be a contributing factor.

TREATMENT - Bathe the foot in a solution of VIRKON S or T.C.P., and then dry it. Rub in some antibiotic cream, (like Aureomycin) and place the bird in a shed or stable with straw or shavings on the floor. Keep the floor as clean as possible, i.e. put the water at the lowest end of the pen. If the bird is badly infected, i.e. there is pus in the wound, a jab of penicillin is advisable. NB This was one of the problems in years gone by when geese and turkeys were walked long distances to towns for market. The farmers got over the problem by either running the birds through liquid or sticky tar to give their feet a protective coating, or by making leather shoes for them.

MORTALITY - None unless the infection spreads.

DIRTY OR STICKY EYE

SIGNS - One or both eyes appearing dirty, vision in the eye obscured, much flicking of the head and rubbing of the eye on the shoulder or base of the neck. Normally seen in winter during cold weather. German Pekins are very prone to this complaint.

CAUSE - This can happen to any breed of duck or goose, but certain individuals seem more prone than others. It is normally caused by lack of adequate washing water, or water that is dirty or frozen over. This is a local infection but it can lead to the loss of an eye.

PREVENTION - Ensure that there is plenty of clean washing water, and keep birds out of windy pens.

STICKY EYE. Often seen in winter during cold and windy periods and when ducks do not have sufficient access to clean water. German Pekins are very prone to this problem.

TREATMENT - Make a mild warm solution of T.C.P. and wash the infected eye twice a day using cotton wool. Pick off any dried on matter very carefully; it is important not to pull away any of the tiny feathers surrounding the eye, or damage the eyelids or workings of the eye. Once clean, dry the area with cotton wool and apply Golden Eye ointment. After a few days, the condition should start to clear up. In bad cases a jab of penicillin may be necessary.

MORTALITY - None unless the infection spreads.

DROPPED TONGUE

SIGNS - Only seen in African and Toulouse geese because of the dewlap or pouch under the lower mandible of the beak. The tongue becomes lodged in the dewlap.

CAUSE - Is unknown but I would suggest it is inherited or caused by too close breeding.

PREVENTION - There is nothing except out crossing your Toulouse or Africans as much as possible.

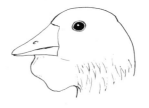

TREATMENT - Depending on the size of dewlap, choose a suitable marble or small stone, and wash it thoroughly. You will need two people for this operation, one to hold the bird, and the second to

SLIPPED TONGUE. And tying up the dewlap to correct the position of the tongue.

remove the tongue from the dewlap, flush out all the remaining debris and clean it as well as possible. Place the marble or stone in the dewlap, and using nylon gut (fishing line) tie with the marble inside. The idea is to shorten and eventually remove the dewlap. The bird will be hopeless to show, but at least it can eat and drink properly.

MORTALITY - Low.

LAMENESS

Lameness is one of the major problems when diagnosing a disease or complaint in ducks and geese. When a bird is sick lameness is frequently the first sign so sometimes it is very difficult to identify the problem: is it external, i.e. has the bird pulled or caught its leg, has it been fighting, is it arthritis or corns; or is it internal, such as worms, stress or a virus? Pick your bird up, check that the legs and feet are working all right, there are no breaks, swellings, or old injuries, and check the weight and condition of the bird. Look at the vent for traces of the colour of the faeces which might give you a clue. Birds will often go lame for some unknown reason, like a sprain perhaps, so monitor that bird and the others around it. If in doubt worm them with Flubenvet.

LEAD POISONING

SIGNS - Birds limping, wings drooping, looking off colour and pale with anaemia (lack of red corpuscles in the blood). Birds may or may not show signs of weight loss. Dark green droppings.

CAUSE - Lead shot from fishing tackle, or lead shot from cartridges. The bird ingests this while fossicking about in the soil, the lead shot enters the gizzard, is ground down and absorbed into the blood stream - one lead shot can kill.

PREVENTION - Although this complaint is rare, it is just as well to think about where your shot will land up when you are potting the odd carrion crow or magpie around your birds. There are now alternatives to lead shot for both fishing and shooting and these should always be recommended.

TREATMENT - Specialist veterinary treatment is required involving a course of injections to neutralise the lead in the blood.

MORTALITY - Medium to high.

MOULT (DUCKS)

Duck are covered in down for approximately 3 - 6 weeks from the date of hatch to when the baby feathers start to grow. This will vary from breed to breed. The young adult feathers grow at 10 - 12 weeks and it is just before this moment that you prepare your ducks for the table, otherwise you are faced with a bird covered with new little quills, the very devil to pull out!

OBSTRUCTIONS

Ducklings, goslings, and adult geese, will attempt to eat and swallow a wide range of materials, so it is very important to keep their pens free of debris such as bits of wire, nails, staples, glass, etc. I once found a goose which had swallowed a length of plastic baler twine. I cut this off at the beak and the bird passed the rest of it and recovered. Very often sharp objects will pierce the wall of the gizzard or intestine and set up Peritonitis resulting in the bird dying of blood poisoning. Adult geese as well as young birds love to find new 'toys' to play with, so you must ensure that everything is safe.

PENIS PARALYSIS OR DROPPED WILLIE SYNDROME

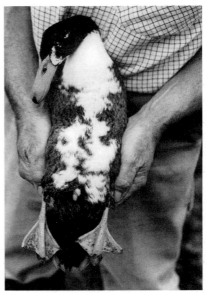

SIGNS - The penis not retracting and the end hanging out, sometimes up to 2" long. Mainly in medium to large ducks including runners and geese. I have never seen this in Call ducks, but that doesn't mean it can't occur in them. The organ becomes dirty and sometimes infection sets in.

CAUSE - The reason for this is unknown; the complaint is uncommon and whether it is caused by lack of swimming water, frosty weather, old age, over exertion or an inherited factor is unclear.

PREVENTION - There is none.

TREATMENT - Often the unretracted organ will wither and atrophy and can then be cut off. Alternatively, it can be washed and dabbed with anti-bacterial lotion and the bird should be kept on clean straw or shavings for at least 2 - 4 weeks until the organ has retracted. The gander or drake should not be used for breeding.

DROPPED WILLIE SYNDROME. This is a Hook Billed drake and the penis has not retracted into the vent but hangs out.

MORTALITY - None unless the area becomes septic.

PROLAPSE

Rare

SIGNS - It appears that some of the insides of the bird are hanging out. This is the oviduct which has been pushed out through the vent, and it is mainly seen in good laying birds like Indian Runners and Khaki Campbells.

CAUSES - There are several: young birds coming into lay too early or a bird passing too large an egg; overweight birds will prolapse, or there could be a defect in the oviduct.

PREVENTION - There is none.

TREATMENT - I have tried several treatments such as pushing the oviduct back and crossing my fingers, or putting a nylon stitch across the bottom of the vent, but eventually the oviduct will come out again. Once the wall of muscle around the vent has been weakened, there is little chance of the oviduct staying in place. Also, it is a very complex area, with not only eggs passing through, but faeces as well.

MORTALITY - High.

PROTRUDING SINUS AIR SACKS

SIGNS - This can be seen from an early age in certain ducks, mainly Calls, certain colours of Indian Runner, and Black East Indians. The sinus sack found under the eye swells up and protrudes. It can be squashed back in with the finger, but comes out again.

CAUSE - I think the cause may be in-breeding, so it would therefore be hereditary, but little is known as to why it appears.

PREVENTION - There is none. It may be wise not to breed from that line of bird.

TREATMENT - None, but keep an eye on the affected bird. One point is that these ducks are particularly susceptible to Mycoplasma; if this sets in (mainly during the winter months), the bird will have difficulty in breathing, it develops

PROTRUDING SINUS. Mainly seen in ducks which are closely bred like Call Ducks and Runners. There is a pronounced swelling under one or both eyes, often squidgy to touch.

a wheeze, and sometimes the sinus cavities fill with mucus and harden. You can always tell, because of the vile smell from the nostrils. A jab of Tylan (approximately ½ cc) in the breast will help, but it will not do anything for the protruding sinuses.

MORTALITY - None unless the bird contracts Mycoplasma when mortality would be low to medium.

SEX CHANGE

When speaking with other breeders on this subject it seems that this problem is occurring more often these days, or perhaps there are more breeders about and so more people are aware of it.

SIGNS – This occurs in adult birds from female to male; I have never seen it the other way round. The female stops laying, moults and then grows male feathers, although the colour may not be exactly the same. The bird even calls like a male, and in the case of ducks, grows the curly feathers on the top of the tail. This is seen in both ducks and geese. Sometimes the bird will only spend one year or season as a male before reverting back to female; sometimes it is a direct response to running all female flocks, and one female takes over the male role and changes accordingly.

CAUSES – There seem to be three main reasons for this: a) Genetic, whereby a bird carries more male genes and is therefore more predisposed to turn into a male if given the opportunity; b) damage through fighting, injury/stress to the reproductive organs, leading to a temporary loss of gender direction; c) toxins; if the birds are swimming in streams and rivers there is a risk from pesticide residues, polychlorinated biphenyls (a toxic pollutant used in the manufacture of plastics) and phthalines (a substance used in the manufacture of dyes and scents). These are known as 'gender benders' and as such will affect the birds' oestrogen levels. They are taken into the system when the bird eats aquatic plants and creatures.

SLIPPED TENDON IN THE LEG (and sometimes the wing)

SIGNS - Normally the lower half of the leg from the hock joint hangs down, with loss of use. It appears that the joint is slightly enlarged. It can also be seen in the pelvic joint. It looks like, and sometimes can be, a dislocation, but is usually a slipped tendon. Sometimes the leg slips out sideways. Sometimes a wing is affected and hangs down lifelessly.

CAUSE - Uncertain, but it is probably caused by a genetic weakness, stress and/or an accident.

PREVENTION - There is none.

TREATMENT - Surgically something may be done, but this would probably be very expensive. I normally cull these birds.

SLIPPED WING or ANGEL WING (more often seen in geese than ducks)

SIGNS - One or both wings start to hang down from about 8 - 10 weeks old. The bird is constantly trying to flick them up into position, but gradually the wings turn outwards away from the body.

CAUSE - An excess of amino acids in the blood, creating a build up of blood in the large flight quills on the wing which in turn makes the wing heavy, and distorts the end section. This is caused by too much protein in the food.

PREVENTION - It is fine to give young goslings protein of up to 17% until 6 weeks old. After that the protein must be reduced to 14% or less.

TREATMENT - On recognising the symptoms, cut the protein in the food immediately; it is best to use straight feed wheat and no pellets at all. Strap up the wing with masking tape, so that it sits neatly against the body: the bird is then unable to stretch the wing . Leave this on for 10 days and then remove it, and repeat if necessary after a day's grace. If caught early, the wing will become normal again. If birds are severely affected, just fatten them up and eat them.

MORTALITY - None, the birds just look awful.

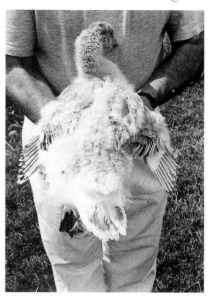

SLIPPED WING or ANGEL WINGS. Just starting on a gosling. Note the flight quills heavy with blood.

STAGGERS/SUN STROKE/HEAT STRESS

SIGNS - The bird or birds appear to be drunk, unsteady on their feet, falling over, sitting down with necks swaying all over the place, or just sitting very quietly and not moving, as though stuffed.

CAUSE - Lack of oxygenated blood to the head. As a bird has no sweat glands, it has to reduce body temperature by breathing harder. If it is unable to reduce its temperature, it goes into a semi-coma and will then die.

PREVENTION - Don't transport birds on very hot days, but if you have to, give them plenty of room, and use the air-conditioning in the car if possible. Goslings are particularly prone to heat stroke, because their downy fluff doesn't offer much protection from the elements. Also, too much water on hot days when they are young can produce sunstroke. Ensure your birds have adequate shade in hot weather, particularly if they are in a house and run.

TREATMENT - Move fast; wrap the birds in wet towels, and put a fan in front to cool them down. Place bowls of water by them, and encourage them to dip their beaks in; it might take several hours for them to come round. It is quite an alarming sight in geese.

MORTALITY - Medium.

STRESS - Loss of use of legs

SIGNS - If a duck or goose has been harried around a pen it will very often lose the use of its legs, or sometimes it will refuse to walk when taken out of its crate or box after travelling. This is often accompanied by watery droppings. Seen in Runners and heavy ducks and geese. Warm or hot days don't help either.

CAUSE - Stress.

PREVENTION - Some breeds and some individual birds are more prone to stress, mainly because of their close breeding. Remember this and handle these breeds or birds accordingly - i.e. it is probably best not to show these birds, and do take extra care when transporting them.

TREATMENT - Place the bird in a safe place, like a stable or large hut, on clean litter (shavings) and with a bowl of clean water. Leave it for up to 12 hours, preferably overnight. Add some liquid vitamins or Protexin to the water after that period if you want to.

MORTALITY - Low.

WET FEATHER

SIGNS - The feathers appear to look untidy and the bird looks bedraggled and waterlogged. It is mainly seen in ducks, and nearly always hand reared birds, but rarely in geese. The duck has difficulty in floating and often has to be rescued from possible drowning.

CAUSE - A lack of oil on the plumage. It is not always clear why. It can be a blocked or infected preening gland. Dirty or foul water can be a contributing factor.

PREVENTION - Clean swimming water is most important, as this gets all the wading and preening instincts going and hopefully starts the preen or oil gland working.

TREATMENT - Inspect the preening gland. It is found on the top of the tail slightly in from the end. It is a raised tuft of feathers, exuding a clear oily liquid. Sometimes this can become swollen and/or blocked. Gently massage it; sometimes it will burst, other times there appears to be nothing wrong. It can be a very frustrating problem, not only for the owner but also for the duck. Keep the bird away from water it might drown in, and be careful in strong sunlight too, as any exposed skin can heat up, leading to sunstroke.

WING CLIPPING (Feather Cutting) & Permanent Pinioning

Although not a disease or problem I have included these, as many people are too nervous or too squeamish to carry them out. It is vitally important that permanent pinioning is used on all *non-indigenous* breeds of wildfowl: in fact, it is the *Law*. Otherwise we would end up with foreign species of duck and geese invading the countryside. We are seeing this now with Canada geese, Carolina and Mandarin ducks and American Stiff Tails for example.

Feather Cutting

This is a temporary measure which is used on domestic duck particularly Calls, miniatures, Black East Indians and Muscovies. Take a pair of strong kitchen scissors and cut the primaries off one wing only, as per diagram. This will unbalance the flight. You must be careful not to cut too much off these feathers, causing the quills to bleed, and also not to cut off too little so the bird can still just fly. This will have to be repeated every year, normally in August.

Wing Clipping

Pinioning at day old

Permanent Pinioning

This is a permanent solution to stop ducks and geese flying, but as stated above, it is only applicable to non-indigenous breeds of wildfowl. Take a sharp pair of scissors and cut off the end portion of one wing as per diagram. This must be done within five days of hatching. The bone in the wing is at this stage quite rubbery. Removing this portion of the wing is removing the area from where the primaries grow, and the bird will never fly away. There should be little mess or bleeding, normally just a small bubble of blood to clot over the wound. Antiseptic spray on this area is advisable on warm days.

GENERAL

Clean swimming water leads to clean birds, better egg production, better fertility and of course fewer or no diseases. A good looking duck i.e. clean, is more attractive to a drake and vice versa. I have seen this so many times when I have cleaned and refilled our plastic ponds: the birds seem to go into overdrive, not only with their preening, but also with their mating. Clean water also ensures that you have fewer problems such as Sticky Eye or Dropped Willie Syndrome.

TURKEYS

Turkeys, particularly pure breeds, are as tough as nuts if reared outdoors and allowed to roam freely. The problems come when you bring them indoors in large numbers.

B =	CAUSED BY A BACTERIA	C =	CHICK 1-4 weeks
V =	CAUSED BY A VIRUS	G =	GROWER 5-17 weeks
P =	CAUSED BY A PROTOZOA	A =	ADULT 18+ weeks

DISEASE	TYPE OF DISEASE	AGE SUSCEPTIBILITY			PAGE
Blackhead	P		G	A	58
Coccidiosis	P	C	G	A	59
E-Coli	B	C	G		59
Erysipelas	B		G	A	60
Fowl cholera	B	C	G	A	61
Mycoplasma	B		G	A	61
Newcastle Disease	V	C	G	A	62
Rhinotracheitis	V		G	A	63
Worms	P		G	A	63

Problems encountered in Turkeys

Bumble Foot	64
Curly Toe Paralysis	64
Fighting	65
Fleas and Lice	65
Impacted Crop	66
Scaley Leg	67

There are quite a few other intensive indoor diseases which I have not mentioned because I think you are unlikely to encounter them. Murphy's Law states your bird will probably contract one of these, but I think it highly unlikely!

Mortality: Is expressed as the number of birds in your flock which are likely to die from the disorder. LOW is 10% and less, MEDIUM is 50% and less, HIGH is 50% and above.

TURKEYS

My experience of turkeys goes back many years and has been mainly concerned with the coloured varieties such as black, bronze, buff, lavender etc. I have had no experience of commercial turkeys and their management.

Given the right surroundings turkeys are as tough as nuts. You have only to see where they come from in central and eastern North America and where they thrive best in this country to realise that. If you have ever been to Norfolk in January you will know what I mean! Turkeys dislike damp, wet conditions, but love to range freely, grazing on grass and berries out of hedgerows, orchards and of course deciduous woodlands. If kept under these conditions they contract very few diseases or complaints. Once you bring them indoors and crowd them, then your problems start. I will not attempt to deal with all the indoor diseases of turkeys as I have no experience of them, but I have mentioned the most likely problems that you might possibly encounter.

BLACKHEAD - (Histomoniasis)

This is the common disease that turkeys contract, along with peafowl, pheasants and partridge. There is a certain hysteria connected with this disease but in reality it is easy to spot and easy to cure.

SIGNS - Young poults (5-10 weeks) looking off colour, not interested in food, mopey, sleepy, and dying within 24-30 hours. Older birds again looking mopey, the tail often stuck up as though they want to discharge all the time, dying within 2-10 days. The tell-tale sign is the bright yellow diarrhoea which smells sulphurous.

CAUSE - Blackhead has nothing to do with the head of the turkey going black. The bird's head might not look its usual vibrant red/blue colour while it is suffering, but don't look for a very discoloured head as a symptom. The disease is caused by a parasite which attacks the large intestine, the caecal tracts and the liver, hence the yellow colour in the droppings. This parasite is called Histomonas meleagridis and is spread by a roundworm called Heterakis, which is mainly found in the caecal tracts. The eggs of Heterakis with the Histomonas parasite on board, are passed through the vent with the droppings and may be eaten later by other birds. Sometimes these eggs can be taken up by earthworms and can remain dormant for long periods, several years, before being ingested either by another turkey or hen, or a wild bird, so you can see what a persistent disease this is.

PREVENTION - There is none, other than moving your birds to fresh ground, and that doesn't always work either. It only needs a blackbird to deposit its droppings on the fresh ground having eaten a worm from the old ground, and you are back to square one. There is a point here - many people say you can't keep hens and turkeys running together on the same ground. This is untrue as I have done it successfully for years, but you must ensure that your birds have a sufficiently extensive range to be able to do so.

What I have found is that turkeys will build up a resistance to Blackhead, particularly if given a preventative dose of Emtryl in the drinking water at the age of 6-8 weeks. This is given for a week, and birds rarely succumb after that age. I am talking about free range birds here.

TREATMENT - Is dimetridazole (trade name Emtryl or Harkanker). You have to move quickly to avoid losses, particularly in young birds. Remove all sources of water, (if necessary move birds away from puddles, ditches, etc) and add dimetridazole to the drinking water; if the poults are weak, dip their beaks in. I have even 'tubed' medicated water into adult birds. Within 24 hours they should be back to normal, and feeding again. Older birds take longer to recover.

On most commercial farms, the turkey food comes in already medicated, not only to combat Blackhead but Coccidiosis as well. This is done mainly because of the huge numbers involved, the short life of the birds, and financial circumstances. But the problem here is that most of these drugs land up on our plates, albeit in minute quantities, although the commercial people counter that they have a medicated feed withdrawal period before the slaughter date. So what has happened? The little grey men from Brussels have stepped in and are trying to ban dimetridazole, because too much is showing up in the food chain; but there is no sensible alternative, so I am not sure what the game farmers and turkey producers will do if this happens.

COCCIDIOSIS - KNOWN AS COXY

SIGNS - Mainly seen in poults when put out to grass, particularly during periods of wet weather or heavy dews. Also in barns where the floor is damp (leaky pipes). Birds are quiet and mopey, with white diarrhoea, (sometimes bloody) and poor growth. Dead birds occurring.

CAUSE - This is a protozoan parasite, of which there are many types. The main group is called Eimeria. The egg or oocyst is passed out through the droppings (an affected bird can produce millions of eggs). The eggs need warm and damp conditions to develop, hence Coccidiosis tends to occur in the autumn or during periods of wet weather in the summer; Coxy can also be found in damp litter indoors. The eggs are eaten by other birds, and then take up residence in the small intestine, duodenum and caecal tracts, where they develop and multiply. The variety or varieties of Coccidiae and their numbers will determine the bird's outlook. Many birds can carry Coccidiae and not be affected, but if the immune system is low, then this will lead to a build up along with other factors (see Stress) and can cause death.

PREVENTION - If you are rearing on grass, make sure it is short, and possibly feed a coccidiostat, ie an anti-coccidiosis drug very often found in turkey food and usually quite unnecessary. Turkeys do build up an immunity to Coccidiosis. Fresh ground helps too.

TREATMENT - If your birds do contract Coxy, the most effective treatment is a drug called Baytox which should clear up the problem. Check with your vet on dosage.

MORTALITY - Can be high.

E-COLI (COLIBACILLOSIS

SIGNS - If you are brooding turkey chicks with hen chicks, and your husbandry is poor, there is a chance that your turkey chicks will pick up E-Coli. The signs are a hunched chick not interested in food or water, wings drooping and runny brown droppings. There is a sweet/sour smell. The odd bird will die.

CAUSE - This is a complex set of microbes which normally live harmoniously in the intestines. When poor hygiene, stale foods, stress and some other disease like

Coccidiosis are present, the E-Coli bacteria go into overdrive, resulting in the death of the bird normally from blood poisoning.

PREVENTION - Because of poor management, it is imperative to put into action a programme of thorough cleaning from the incubator right through to the rearing equipment. The main causes of E-Coli are stale or badly stored food, poor hygiene and stress. Stress in this case nearly always means overcrowding, or draughty or poorly ventilated rearing rooms.

TREATMENT - The use of probiotics in chick food or water has been a godsend, and now in America they are using probiotics to sort out Salmonellas. Add Protexin to the food or better still to the water, and it will soon clear up the E-Coli, providing the hygiene and food are good; I have seen this turn a poor batch of chicks around from being rather weedy birds to very healthy chicks. What this does is rearrange the flora in the gut of the bird, suppressing the harmful ones and promoting the good ones.

MORTALITY - Low to medium.

ERYSIPELAS

This is not a common disease, but farmers who use barns which used to house sheep or pigs, should be aware of it.

SIGNS - This disease is mainly seen in young adult birds, very often when they are ready for killing. A few birds die for no apparent reason, but closer inspection will reveal that they have slightly swollen and discoloured heads and large skin blisters under the wings and on the breast. It can be a serious problem.

CAUSE - This is caused by the bacteria called Erysipelothrix; Rhusiopathiae is mainly found in pigs. This bacteria remains in the soil for long periods, hence the problems with using old farm buildings for rearing turkeys. The disease is zoonotic, which means that it can pass from pigs to turkeys to humans, so be careful about handling birds with this disease, as it is thought that it is contracted through cuts and abrasions on the birds and your hands.

PREVENTION - If you are using old farm buildings or buildings that have housed livestock other than turkeys, or have been used for lambing perhaps, then a good programme of disinfection is required. Having said that, I have had free range turkeys die of this disease, only because they foraged over an area where pigs had been kept many years before.

TREATMENT - This is with penicillin, if you can catch the bird in time before it dies.

MORTALITY - Low to medium.

FOWL CHOLERA

This is another zoonotic disease. Although rare, it is worth being aware of; it is also notifiable. Turkeys are more susceptible than chickens

SIGNS - This is a rare disease now, so it is unlikely that your birds will contract it, but it is sensible to know about it and be able to recognize it. Outbreaks occur mainly during heatwaves and when birds are stressed by heat. The birds look mopey with a discharge from the nostrils and watery green or white diarrhoea, and they die rather quickly with the severe form of the disease. In the less severe or chronic form, mortality is less, birds appear to have swollen heads and breathe with difficulty.

CAUSE - It is caused by the bacteria Pasteurella multocida which comes in various strains. The disease is transmitted from bird to bird by contamination from a carrier bird, wild birds or vermin, by water, people, equipment, food bags, vehicles etc. As you can see, it is very contagious.

PREVENTION - There is none. Listen to any reports of outbreaks in your area, and be careful where you buy your stock from. Good husbandry and cleaning programmes are essential.

TREATMENT - Although it can be treated with sulphur based drugs like Sulphamezathine, the problem remains that your birds may become carriers. As it is a notifiable disease, there is a total slaughter programme.

MORTALITY - In the severe form it is high, but otherwise mortality is low to medium.

MYCOPLASMA

SIGNS - This is one of the few diseases that turkeys catch and/or inherit. It is very noticeable, and begins with a nasal discharge, or a bubbly mucus in the corner of the eye or eyes, followed by swellings under the eye. These are soft at first but will harden in time. The eye or eyes will close, although the bird will continue to feed, listening to other members of the flock. The bird seems to breathe through its mouth, as the nasal and sinus area is blocked with a foul smelling discharge. The bird looks awful in the advanced stages, with one or both eyes badly swollen, a gaping beak, and often a distorted face.

CAUSE - This is a bacteria called Mycoplasma gallisepticum. It is spread from bird to bird by sneezing and in the drinking water. I believe that susceptibility to this disease is inherited because of the way it spreads, but I have no proof of this. It can be transmitted through the egg.

PREVENTION - Try to buy uninfected stock, although this is sometimes difficult when choosing coloured breeds. Nostril sniffing is a good idea, but it is not entirely fool-proof.

TREATMENT - Although you can treat this disease with antibiotics, like Terramycin, Tylan Soluble or Aureomycin, it only suppresses it and it sometimes recurs. Certain strains of Mycoplasma are resistant to certain antibiotics, so it is worth taking the bird to the vet to have it swabbed, before deciding which antibiotic to use. If the bird is badly infected, and the swellings under the eyes are hard, it is possible to remove these by making a cut under the swelling, and a foul smelling cheesy substance normally pops out. (This obviously has to be done in the surgery).

MORTALITY - Normally low.

NEWCASTLE DISEASE OR FOWL PEST

You are unlikely to encounter this disease unless there is a national outbreak, which you will hear about anyway. The disease is notifiable which means that, should you think you have the symptoms among your birds, you must contact your local vet or your local MAFF vet immediately.

SIGNS - Are variable, including the necks twisted around, birds flopping about unable to stand, or just twitching. Sometimes there is difficulty in breathing and often a discharge from both ends. Egg production will drop also, there can be high mortality, or only a few birds dying.

CAUSE - There are several strains of this virus, which is part of the Paramyxovirus group. The various viruses will affect all domestic fowl and some wild birds like sparrows and pigeons, so you can see the potential dangers here. The disease attacks the nervous and respiratory systems, hence the lack of co-ordination in the birds. The big worry about this disease is that it can be spread in so many ways, in the wind, physically on boots, crates, feed bags and vehicles, by wild birds and migrating birds and also sometimes in egg form, but this is considered rare.

PREVENTION - If there is cause for alarm, and the disease is in the country and spreading, then you can quite simply vaccinate your flock, be it chickens, ducks, turkeys or pheasants. This treatment is inexpensive, but remember that vaccination is not 100% effective, although it certainly helps. There are two easy ways to vaccinate your flock, either through the drinking water or by spraying your birds with a fine mist so that it is absorbed through the eye.

TREATMENT - There is none, and if your flock becomes infected, there will be a mandatory slaughter programme of all the birds in your area.

MORTALITY - This is of no consequence, because if your turkeys contract the disease you lose everything anyway. In reality mortality can be low and birds do recover from Newcastle Disease, but they are carriers for life having once been infected.

RHINOTRACHEITIS

As the name states, inflammation of the nasal area (rhino) and the windpipe (trachea). This disease is rarely seen in free range birds.

SIGNS - Birds from poults to adults build up mucus in the windpipe and nasal area, causing them to rattle, sneeze and snick and there is even a change of voice from the stags who become unable to gobble normally. This disease can be confused with Mycoplasma, but sometimes has a higher mortality rate.

CAUSE - This is a pneumovirus.

PREVENTION - Most of the large turkey producers vaccinate against this disease, and you are strongly recommended to do the same for semi-intensive production of turkeys.

TREATMENT - There is no treatment. Once your turkeys have had the disease it is difficult to stop it from returning unless you have a very rigid disinfectant programme.

MORTALITY - Low to medium.

WORMS

SIGNS - Birds appear listless, sometimes not interested in food, sometimes ravenously hungry, they lose weight and the breast bone feels very sharp. The droppings can be whitish (not to be confused with Coccidiosis) and as the infestation continues the droppings turn light green; the birds eventually die, and this can take some weeks.

CAUSE - Turkeys can suffer from a variety of worms, but the main types are caecal, gape and tape worms. The caecal worm (Heterakis gallinae) is found in the caecal tracts or blind gut, and is white and up to ½ inch long (1cm). This is the worm which helps the spread of the parasite which causes Blackhead. Gape worm (Syngamus trachea) is found in the windpipe; it is red in colour and about 1 inch (2cms) long. It is not very common in turkeys but causes them to gasp and struggle to breathe as the worms take over the windpipe. Tape worms (Cestoda) are quite common in turkeys; they are white, flat and ribbon shaped and can be up to 10 inches (25 cms) long.

PREVENTION - Turkeys can live quite well with a certain worm burden. They are always going to be exposed to worms, not only from wild birds but also from insects, worms, beetles, etc so free range turkeys should be wormed regularly. Some people worm annually, some every six months, and others never.

TREATMENT - Luckily Flubenvet clears out all the worms found in poultry, and is a very safe drug. It is a fine white powder which you add to the food, be it in pellet or meal or grain form. It is best to pour a little cooking oil over the food so that the Flubenvet will stick to it. Dosage: 1 teaspoon per each feed for 12 birds for seven days (the dosage does not have to be very precise). Don't eat the eggs during this period and obviously don't kill any of the turkeys for eating either. I try to worm them in an area like a shed or stable, keeping them in so that the dead worms can be collected and disposed of.

MORTALITY - Medium.

BUMBLE FOOT

This is common among turkeys, particularly the heavier birds.

SIGNS - Swellings around the ankle and foot pad, often with lameness which can become bad.

CAUSE - Birds coming down from roost and landing badly on insufficient and/or wet litter. This is why heavy stag birds are not given any perches in turkey breeding centres. Cuts and abrasions to the feet will also cause Bumble Foot.

PREVENTION - Lower perches, perhaps no more than 18" or 45 cm high and a good thick bedding of straw or shavings to land on.

TREATMENT - This is a difficult area to treat, and more often than not there is a swelling which has no visible cause. If this is the case, give the bird a jab of penicillin. The swelling will remain, but the lameness will improve. If there is a scab then the swelling can be cleaned of any pus and again, penicillin given. The bird should be placed in a large pen with clean straw or shavings. There is no need to bandage the foot, as, (a) it is difficult and (b) the bandage soon becomes dirty and infected. Best to leave the wound open, and puff it with wound powder.

MORTALITY - Normally nil.

CURLY TOES OR CURLY TOE PARALYSIS

Because a turkey's foot is large, curly toes are very obvious.

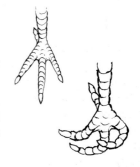

SIGNS - This complaint can be seen at day old, sometimes on one foot, sometimes on both. The chick moves around normally but its appearance is distressing. The toes are bent or crooked.

CAUSE - There are three possible causes. It can be genetic, there may be a vitamin deficiency in the food, or infra red bulbs may have been used as a source of heat over the young birds.

PREVENTION - Curly toes can be transmitted through the egg into the embryo, so always check your breeding stock for birds with curly toes, or a tendency to breed chicks with curly toes. Check that the food is fresh, and the sell-by date is in order. Curly Toe Paralysis is often caused by a lack of riboflavin in the diet which is again transmitted through the egg into the embryo. The same problem can occur with young chicks, so freshness and quality of food is paramount. I have seen curly toes develop after hatching, particularly when white infra red bulbs (the 250v kind) are used. Never put the food near these bulbs as they tend to cook it and it will lose its nutritional value as a result.

TREATMENT - Most people will cull these chicks, but if the birds are for eating they will survive. There is a treatment for this if you have the time and patience. See Curly Toes, Hens.

MORTALITY - Normally zero.

FIGHTING

This is not a disease but it can be a serious problem. Turkeys are bully boys not only with their own species but also with other breeds, and it is not confined to the males as the females are as bad. Large commercial establishments overcome this by subdued lighting, but with free range and barn reared birds it can be a problem. At the end of the day it is all about carcass damage, either from the beaks or the toe nails. Although stress can be a contributory factor, I have seen the most non-stressed birds battling it out until one bird or both become too exhausted to carry on. Often if one bird is being attacked and goes down, the others will be merciless about treading it into the ground. This is when damage occurs and sometimes death. As well as using the wings as clubs, birds often lock beaks or pull each others snoods or noses off - very violent to watch.

In my experience, the only way to stop this is to separate habitual fighters. If the management is correct, fighting should be minimal but you must be aware of this potential problem.

FLEAS & LICE -

SIGNS - Pick up the turkey and look among the feathers, particularly around the vent area where they are fluffy. Birds will often stand around looking unhappy; fleas and lice are a cause of infertility in male or stag birds, and broody hen turkeys will leave their nests if plagued with fleas. One of the tell-tale signs is white clusters of lice eggs on the base of the quills around the vent area.

DERMANYSSUS GALLINAE, Red Mite, actual size about 1mm. Sucks blood at night, lives in cracks in the woodwork during the day - a whiteish powder betrays its presence. Worst in warm weather. Makes the birds anaemic.

CAUSE - Fleas live on the bird, but deposit their eggs around the turkey house on the floor or in the nest box. Lice, which are yellowish brown in colour and wingless, live continuously on the birds, hence the white clusters of eggs on the feathers. Fleas suck blood from the bird, thus causing anaemia (the birds look pale and shrivelled about the face through lack of red blood cells); lice mainly feed on feathers and skin debris.

PREVENTION - Check your birds regularly, particularly in the summer months. This means handling each bird.

TREATMENT - Today, Pyrethrum powder is used for the control of fleas and lice. It is an excellent product, but keep it away from water, as it kills fish and aquatic life. Pick your bird up, pull off any clusters of eggs by giving the affected feathers a sharp tug, and then burn them. Dust the bird with flea powder around the vent area, under the wings and along the neck and back. You will notice the dead fleas and lice falling off. Repeat after a week.

MORTALITY - Normally nil.

MENOPON GALLINAE, Common Fowl Louse, lives on skin debris and feathers. Irritant. About 2mm long, yellow. Eggs (nits) are laid on feathers.

LICE EGGS on the base of feathers around the vent area of the bird.

IMPACTED CROP

SIGNS – Young turkey chicks with full and firm crops, standing about, slightly listless to start off with and dying after two or three days.

CAUSE – When turkeys are chicks they are often shy feeders and drinkers, so coloured marbles are sometimes placed in the food and water to encourage them. They will occasionally eat their bedding rather than food, so on no account bed them on hay or feed them grass which they love, as this will cause the crop to impact.

PREVENTION – Just feed turkey chicks on Turkey Starter Crumbs and cage bird grit.

TREATMENT – There is none.

MORTALITY – Medium to high.

SCALEY LEG

Not often seen on turkeys, but it can occur as a result of keeping chickens and turkeys together.

SIGNS - Scales lifting up on the toes and legs.

CAUSE - Scaley leg is caused by a mite called Cnemidocoptes mutans, which lives under the scales of the leg and toes of the bird. The mite spreads along the perch from bird to bird.

PREVENTION - Regular cleaning and disinfecting of the perches and houses.

TREATMENT - This will take two people, one to hold the bird and the other to paint the legs and toes with surgical spirit. Use a soft small 1" or 2cm brush and work it well into the scales. Do this once a week for five weeks.

MORTALITY - Should be nil, unless the bird is left without treatment.

WHAT CAN I CATCH FROM MY BIRDS?

Quite a few people have telephoned me very worried that their children might catch some dreadful disease from their own or their neighbour's ducks or hens. The answer to this is that it is highly unlikely. You are more liable to catch something from your dog or cat than you are from your birds.

Having said that however, some people are more susceptible than others to certain viruses, bacteria, fungi or parasites carried by birds. When the salmonella debacle was raging a few years ago, people were told all sorts of nonsense, mainly by professors and so-called experts. There are a great many strains of salmonella, some more virulent than others, and we all carry it in our bodies and take in more with a variety of different foods that we eat; but we take the precaution of not giving the vulnerable members of the family, i.e. the young or the old, raw eggs, partly cooked eggs, or of course badly defrosted or cooked chicken.

So which are the diseases which are zoonotic? (i.e. they can cross over from bird to man).

Psittacosis or Ornithosis - Probably the most well known, is a flu-like complaint leading to death in man, but you would have to work in a factory handling thousands of birds before you became infected. You are more likely to catch it from the family budgerigar or parrot than from your pet hen.

Avian TB - I have mentioned this under Duck and Geese and I know of one rare case when this was contracted. The person involved was handling and recording dozens of birds in a large wildfowl collection.

Duck Virus - I did see the other day that a woman had caught conjunctivitis from her ducks which had an influenza virus. Again this must be rare.

Favus - Mainly found in the tropics and very rare in this country, Favus is a form of poultry ringworm which produces a most offensive smell and a whitish, fungus-like growth round the face and wattles of the bird.

Newcastle Disease - You will know if this disease is about because it is notifiable to MAFF etc. but there have been rare cases of humans contracting it, probably from handling infected birds. Conjunctivitis is the first sign.

Erysipelas - A turkey/pig disease which can cross to man and is called Erysipeloid. It is spread by cuts or sores on the hands. Again very rare.

Bird Fancier Lung - Mainly a complaint of pigeon and small bird keepers. I have known several people in the poultry world with this disease. It is like a form of emphysema or asthma; there is a shortage of breath whilst in contact with feathers, feather dust, or birds.

Fleas/Lice/Mites - This is probably where most people experience the cross-over effect, particularly in the hair and on the hands and arms. Some people are more affected than others, being badly bitten, while other people merely suffer from itchy scalps.

THE RESPIRATORY PARTS OF A CHICKEN

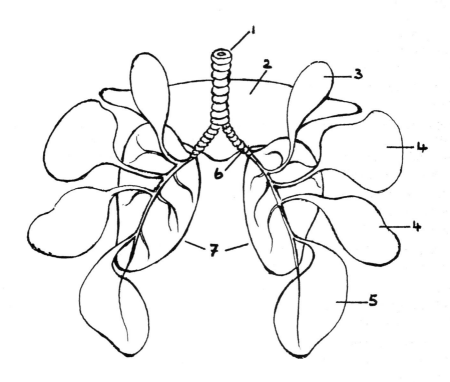

1)	Trachea or Windpipe	2)	Clavicular Sac
3)	Cervical Sac	4)	Thoracic Sac
5)	Abdominal Sac	6)	Bronchial Canal
7)	Lungs		

SIGNS OF GOOD HEALTH

PHYSICAL: **COMB** - Correct size and colour
EYES - Bright and clear
GAIT - Alert and upright
FEATHERS - Smooth, shiny and in place
TAIL - Carried correctly
LEGS - Clean
NO FLEAS OR LICE
BREATHING - Good, not rattling, no discharges
DROPPINGS - Firm and dark with white tip
BODYWEIGHT - Correct for age
SMELL - Smells warm and pleasant (sniff nostrils and vent)

BEHAVIOUR: **NOISES** - Calm, contented
FEEDING
DRINKING
LAYING OR PUTTING ON WEIGHT
MOVING AROUND
PREENING
PERCHING
DUST OR SUN BATHING
SPARRING OR MOCK FIGHTING - In young birds

The health of a bird can also be judged by the warmth of its feet. If a bird is standing around in cold mud or water, it will obviously get cold, its body temperature will drop and it will be far more susceptible to disease. The high body temperature of a chicken (103 degrees) means it can cope with most bacteria. This is essential as the chicken is a scavenger feeder.

WHAT TO CHECK WHEN CONFRONTED WITH A SICK BIRD

1) WEIGHT - When picking the bird up, what is the body weight like? Does it feel skeletal?

If yes, the problem could be worms, mal or poor nutrition, possibly a vitamin or mineral deficiency, or chronic disease.

2) BITES & BREAKAGES -Inspect the bird for any puncture wounds from fox or dog bites: mink and stoats leave tiny puncture marks on the neck. Is a wing hanging down, or is there an obvious break in a wing or leg? Can the bird walk or stretch its wings? Has it a slipped wing or tendon?

3) PARASITES - While inspecting the birds check also for fleas, lice and possibly ticks. Treat accordingly. Are the feathers dirty? - Northern Fowl Mite.

4) COLOUR - Does the bird's comb look discoloured, mauve, yellowish or white? Mauve indicates stress and/or heart problems, yellowish or white will indicate chronic diseases or anaemia caused by parasites.

5) BLEEDING - Birds bleed profusely from the comb, wattles, head area and feet. If possible hold the bleeding part under a really cold running tap or apply cotton wool. Wound Powder helps to staunch blood, so does a cobweb. If you want blood for a Salmonella pullorum test, puncture one of the veins which are easily visible on the inside of the wing.

6) LEGS - Covered in crusty white scales that look like bark - Scaley legs.

7) FEET - Swollen at the ankle joint or under the foot: Bumble Foot. Under the foot: Corns or injury.

8) FEATHERS - If a duck is wet and cannot float: Wet Feather.

9) LUMPS & BUMPS - Feel carefully around the breast, abdomen and wings for lumps. It could be a number of things: egg bound, Water Belly, a tumor or possibly cancer.

10) BREATHING - Laboured breathing due to blockage: Avian diphtheria, Gape Worm or a chronic respiratory problem or disease. Is the bird rattling or gurgling as it breathes? It could possibly have one of the respiratory diseases like Mycoplasma.

11) EYES - Mucus in the corner, swollen under the eye: Mycoplasma.

12) CROP - Hard or soft, enlarged: Sour or impacted crop.

13) SMELL - Smell the bird's nostrils - if they smell putrid, this is a sign of Mycoplasma.

14) DROPPINGS - Look in the box that the bird arrived in and then look at the page under DROPPINGS.

This is just a quick guide for when you are confronted with a sick bird, but more often than not it is an internal problem that you can't see without opening the bird up. If you have a number of birds with the same complaint try to take a live one to the vet for post-mortem or autopsy. A sick live bird is best as it can be put down, and then the fresh carcass can be investigated. Time is an important factor for autopsy as the longer the bird has been dead, the more difficult it is to diagnose the problem.

DROPPINGS

One of the best indications of a bird's health is its droppings. Just as some Chinese doctors can see from the colour of your tongue what is going on inside you, so droppings from chickens, ducks, geese and turkeys are also important.

Here is a guide, albeit a very rough one. Chickens make two kinds of droppings, ceacal and intestinal.

Droppings with blood - Coccidiosis

Greenish droppings - Late stages of worms

White, milky runny droppings - Worms, Coccidiosis, Gumboro

Brown runny droppings - E-Coli

Clear or watery runny droppings - Stress & I.B.

Yellow and foamy droppings - Coccidiosis

Bright yellow and runny - Blackhead (more in turkeys than chickens)

Greyish white & running continuously - Vent Gleet

White pasty material is mainly Uric Acid, which is urine

Red/orange matter seen in the droppings. This is part of the lining of the stomach, which is shed sometimes.

The best sort of dropping is dark and firm with a white tip. Broodies will make copious, fibrous, smelly droppings. Droppings will change according to the food the birds are given, and the access to their surroundings.

STRESS

Because many rare breeds of chickens are very inbred their susceptibility to disease is high, hence you must expect losses, and there will probably have to be some culling because of deformities. I have found that if you minimise the stress, i.e. your management is good, and your foodstuff is good, the birds will thrive, albeit their vigour is often poor because of inbreeding. If the birds are stressed and in a competitive environment, i.e. if you are rearing too many together and with other breeds, this is where the problems start to accumulate. In the diagram below I show the sort of problems encountered, which are compounded if you are rearing on ground that has been used for poultry before.

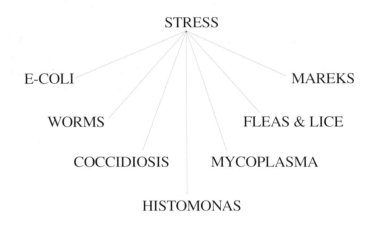

The problems begin when your young birds start to look mopey, and you are not sure what is wrong with them, as some of the symptoms are very similar. Then you are not sure what to treat them with and whether they have x or y, or maybe x and y. They can often have a viral infection together with a bacterial infection and, because they are unhealthy, a parasite problem as well.

If you don't think you have Mareks, i.e. you haven't brought in any possible Mareks carriers and your young birds are well separated from your adult stock, my advice is to worm them with Flubenvet which also has the knock-on effect of subduing Coccidiosis. Put the birds onto fresh, clean, short grass, or clean shavings, and worm them for seven days. Cull and burn any weak birds that obviously aren't going to make it, and if you can afford it, take a couple down to the vet (specialist avian vet) for a post-mortem. You can take them live, as the vet can get a better result from a live bird.

Having wormed them, take stock and see how they look. Weighing them during this period is a good indication of their progress. If the birds are still poor doers, then you certainly need a post-mortem. If they look brighter, leave them for seven days and then if they are still not fully recovered, put some Terramycin in the water, the full dose for 7 days and ½ dose for the next seven days. You should now see a difference in the birds, but you still may have to cull some of them. Now let their immune systems build up. I don't like giving birds drugs unless I have to, and these foodstuffs with built-in antibiotics are a complete no no to me. So it is a combination of trial and error with the drugs available, and also working closely with your vet on the results of his post mortem. It is not a bad idea to keep a diary, so that if, during the following year or so, the same situation arises, you will know how to deal with it. You will always find that problems increase at the end of the season, whereas the early season's birds romp away.

Many people make the mistake of hatching and rearing for too long. It is far better to have a short rearing season than one that trails on for months and months. The key to success is hygiene, and it's important to allow the rearing equipment to rest out in the sun and wind for as long as possible between seasons.

KILLING BIRDS

There are times where you need to despatch or kill a bird, not only for human consumption but also to put it out of its misery.

Not many people today know how to wring a bird's neck, and this is a technique which requires 'hands on' instruction if the bird is not to suffer. I have therefore listed several ways in which to kill a bird satisfactorily without causing any suffering.

Killing a turkey with an airgun

A) If your bird is small like a bantam, small hen or duck, then Semark Pliers can be used satisfactorily. Place the bird under your arm, and hold it with one hand; with the other put the pliers round the neck and squeeze. The pliers sever the vertibrae instantly. Hold the bird firmly to control flapping wings, while keeping the pliers closed for 20 seconds, after which time the bird will be limp and dead.

B) For larger birds like big cockerels, ducks, geese and turkeys, an air-gun works well. Hold the bird by its legs and allow the head to rest against the ground or a bale of straw. Point the muzzle of the gun close to the back of the head and fire. You should find there is very little flapping of the wings as the air-gun pellet has passed through the nerve cortex at the back of the brain.

C) For geese, ducks and turkeys, the broom handle method is effective if you are strong and tall enough. Hold the bird by its legs with its head and neck resting on a hard or concrete floor. Place the broom handle across the neck, and stand on the handle with one foot each side of the head, at the same time jerking upwards with the legs thus breaking the neck. This is clean and quick but you do need to be strong.

An alternative method of killing larger poultry

D) This is the method I prefer to use. Take a piece of wood 2 feet long and approximately 1 ½" square, (a piece of tiling lathe is good), hold the bird in your left hand, if right handed, and strike the bird hard on the back/top of the head with the piece of wood. You may need to repeat the blow, to make quite sure. If blood comes from the beak and nostrils, it is a sign that the bird is dead. This method is particularly good on youngstock, as their skulls are thinner and softer. On a lighter note, it always amuses me that the same system is used to kill fish, and the piece of wood is called a 'priest'.

E) If you are at the vet's surgery, then the standard method of a lethal dose of anasthetic will be the cleanest way of dispatching your bird.

Always kill birds out of sight of other birds.

GENERAL NOTES

CONGENITAL. - denoting or relating to any non-hereditary condition i.e. an abnormality existing at birth.

HEREDITARY. - relating to factors that can be transmitted genetically from one generation to another.

Weak or sick birds will be subject to attack from other birds, particularly older cock birds which will try to tread them.

Don't mix drugs: use one drug at a time.

I do not believe in in-feed medication. This reduces the bird's immunity to disease, and poisons the carcass and/or eggs. If a bird has a particular complaint it should be treated with a drug or medicine for that complaint, and the withdrawal times should be observed for that drug.

Ground will become sour if there is not a good rotation of other livestock or crops. On the small scale it is better to have your birds in a shed on a deep litter system during the winter, in order to check a build-up of disease, to give the ground a rest, and to avoid muddy conditions.

Birds walking away and backwards, head sometimes lowered. This is seen in growers, where the bird has been pecked on the head, causing mild brain damage. It normally recovers.

White feathers on older birds, particularly on the head and neck, often denote some injury caused by mating or fighting.

Birds that become friendly often have a chronic illness. It seems as if they somehow know that you might be able to help them, and are prepared to give up their independence.

Star Gazers are chicks that stand and stare upwards with their beaks pointing at the sky, slightly shaking their heads. This is a condition called ENCEPHALAMASIA and the chicks must be culled. It is quite rare.

A three legged cockerel as illustrated by Ullise Aldrovandi (1522-1605) from Bologna, Italy.

DISEASES	AND THEIR OTHER NAMES
ASPERGILLOSIS	Mycotic pneumonia, Pneumomycosis, Mycosis
AVIAN LEUCOSIS	Lymphomatosis, Leucosis
BOTULISM	Limberneck, Botulinum toxic disease
CANDIDIASIS	Sour Crop, Thrush
CHLAMYDIOSIS	Ornithosis, Psittacosis
COLIBACILLOSIS	E-Coli, Escherichia coli infection, Coliform, Coli septicaemia
DUCK VIRUS ENTERITIS	Duck plague
HISTOMONIASIS	Blackhead, Enterohepatitis
MYCOPLASMOSIS	Sinusitis, Coryza, Synovitis
MYCOTOXICOSIS	Aflatoxin poisoning, Fungal toxin poisoning
NEWCASTLE DISEASE	Fowl pest
PASTEURELLOSIS	Yersiniosis, Pseudotuberculosis fowl cholera
SALMONELLOSIS	Fowl typhoid, Salmonella pullorum, Bacillary white diarrhoea
WORMS	Round, Flat, Tape & Hairworms, Helminths, Nematodes

IS THIS THE FIRST RECORDED DISEASE ?

"But the worst enemy of every kind is the pip, and especially between the time of harvest and vintage. The cure is in hunger, and they must lie in smoke, at all events if it be produced from bay-leaves or savin, a feather being inserted right through the nostrils and shifted daily; diet garlic mixed with spelt, either steeped in water in which an owl has been dipped or else boiled with white vine seed and certain other substances."

This was state of the art medicine in Roman times as recorded by Pliny (63BC -113AD). Savin is a species of juniper and Spelt is an old species of wheat. I am sure the bird, if it had succumbed, would have tasted delicious! The word "Pip" is translated from Pituita (Latin) which means Phelom or Rheum. This might be the first record of Micoplasma.

VETERINARY TERMS	PLAIN ENGLISH
ACUTE	Severe
AFLATOXIN	A fungal toxin poisoning mainly from grain
AGGLUTINATION	Clumping together of cells in a fluid
ANTI-BODY	A substance in the blood which helps fight against harmful bacteria, viruses, toxins, etc
ASPHYXIATION	Suffocation
ATROPHY	Withering or wasting of an organ or tissue
AUTOPSY	Post-mortem. Investigation after death
AVIAN	Concerning birds
CAPILLARIES	Small blood vessels
CARRIER	A bird which is infected by a disease but shows no signs of that disease
CASEOUS	Firm, cheese like
CHRONIC	Slow, prolonged
COMMENSAL	Where two organisms live together on one host, but neither suffers
CONJUNCTIVITIS	Inflammation of the membrane in the front of the eye
CYANOSIS	Blueness in the face and comb, denoting lack of oxygen in the blood
DEHYDRATED	Tissue or body dried out
EMACIATION	Extreme thinness
ENTERITIS	Inflammation of the intestines
EXUDATE	Fluid which seeps into the body cavity or out of tissue as a result of an accident or disease
FEBRILE	Relating to fever or feverish
FRIABLE	Soft material which breaks up easily
HEPATITIS	Inflammation of the liver

HISTOLOGY	Microscopic inspection of tissue, etc
IMPACTION	Where food or material has become tightly packed into an organ or part of a bird
INCUBATION PERIOD	The time between the bird picking up a disease and showing signs of that disease
INGESTION	Eating or intake of food or material
LESION	Changes produced by diseases in organs or tissues
MORTALITY	Death rate
MUCUS	Slimy secretion from eyes and nostrils, produced by mucus membrane
NECROSIS OR NECROTIC	Area (of tissue) which has died
NEOPLASM	New growth as applied to tumours
NEURAL	Concerning nerves
NODULE	A (small) solid mass attached to an organ or tissue
OEDEMA	Fluid which accumulates under the skin in an organ, body cavity or tissue
PATHOGEN OR PATHOGENIC	An agent that causes a disease
PERACUTE	Very severe
PERICARDIUM	The membrane which surrounds the heart
PERICARDITIS	Inflammation of the pericardium
PERITONITIS	Inflammation of the peritoneum, the membrane lining the abdominal cavity
PEROSIS	Slipped tendon
PROTOZOA	A tiny single cell organism
RHINO, RHINITIC	Nasal, to do with the nose
SARCOMA	Cancerous growth or tumour

SEPTICAEMIA	A condition of the blood stream when filled with harmful bacteria, blood poisoning
SEROLOGY	Testing blood for anti-bodies
SUBCLINICAL	When the disease is so slight as not to be recognisable
SUBCUTANEOUS	Under the skin, as in injections
SYNDROME	A group of symptoms, not always attributable to a single cause
TOXAEMIA	The presence of toxins in the blood
TRACHEA, TREACHEITIS	Windpipe, inflammation of
URATES, UREATES	Chalky white material from the kidneys deposited in the droppings
VECTOR	A carrier of disease (snail, water, etc)
ZOONOSIS, ZOONOTIC	A disease which can transfer from bird or animal to humans

∧. three legged cockerel as illustrated by Ullise Aldrovandi (1522-1605) from Bologna, Italy

LIST OF VETERINARY SURGEONS
ENGLAND

AVON
J R Best, The Vet Surgery, 32 West Hill, PORTISHEAD, Bristol, BS20 9LN
Tel - 01275 847400   Avian
                            P.M.'s

BERKSHIRE
Mr S W Cooke, Avian & Exotic Vet. Centre, Kelperland Vet. Group, Ascot Road,
Touchenend, MAIDENHEAD, Berkshire, SL6 3LA
Tel - 01628 24935   Spec. interest in poultry
                           Avian
                           P.M.'s

CAMBS
K Gooderham, Marsh Lane, Hemingford Grey, HUNTINGDON, Cambs PE18 9EN
Tel - 01480 62816   Spec. interest in poultry
                           Avian
                           P.M.'s

CHESHIRE
Ian Cameron, Manor Court Vet. Centre, Church St, TARVIN, Cheshire, CH2 8EB
Tel - 01829 40639   Unsure

B Coles, Cranmore Vet. Centre, 140 Chester Road, CHILDER THORNTON,
Wirral, Cheshire, L66 1QN
Tel - 0151 339 9141   Spec. interest in poultry
                             Avian
                             P.M's

DEVON
Mrs S Lewis-Jones, 5 High Street, HONITON, Devon
Tel - 01404 42657   Avian
                           P.M.'s

D J Shingleton, Waterman Farm, Ugborough, IVYBRIDGE, S Devon, PL21 0PB
Tel - 01548 830552   Spec. in poultry
                            Avian
                            P.M.'s

Mr R Turner, St Davids Vet. Group, Marsh Barton Farm, Clyst St George, EXETER, EX3 0QH
Tel - 01392 876622   Spec. in poultry
                            P.M.'s

DORSET
Mr T M Phillips, St Marys Vet. Clinic, 300 Ringwood Rd, FERNDOWN, BH22 8DX
Tel - 01202 876901   Avian

ESSEX
M P Lawton, 12 Fitzilian Ave, Harold Wood, ROMFORD, Essex, RM3 0QS
Tel - 01708 384444   Avian
                            P.M.'s

Blackwater Vet. Group, Lion Cottage, Maypole Rd, TIPTREE, Colchester, CO5 0EJ
Tel - 01206 818282   Avian
                            P.M.'s

H Hellig & Partners, 14 Church Lane, COLCHESTER, CO3 4AF
Tel - 01206 48516   Spec. in poultry
                            Avian
                            P.M.'s

GLOS
R W Blowey, Glos. Labs, St Oswalds Road, GLOUCESTER, GL1 2SJ
Tel - 01452 524961   Spec. in poultry
                            Avian
                            P.M.'s

R S Broadbent, Stow Vet. Surgns, Backwalls, STOW-ON-THE-WOLD, GL54 1DS
Tel - 01451 830620   Spec. in poultry
                            Avian
                            P.M.'s

N A Forbes, The Clock House Vet. Hosp, Wallbridge, STROUD, Glos, GL5 3JD
Tel - 01453 672555   Spec. in poultry
                            Avian
                            P.M.'s

HAMPSHIRE
Mr P W Scott, Keanter, Stoke Charity Rd, Kings Worthy, WINCHESTER, SO23 7LS
Tel - 01962 883895   Avian
                            P.M.'s

HEREFORD
P W Laing, 40 Etnam Street, LEOMINSTER, Herefordshire, HR6 8AQ
Tel - 01568 613232   Spec. in poultry & game birds
                                    Avian
                                    P.M.'s

Mrs S E Pattison, Westmoor Veterinary Services, Mortimer Cottage, Westmoor,
MANSEL LACY, Hereford, HR4 7HN
Tel - 01981 590603   Spec. in poultry & game birds
                                    P.M.'s

HERTS
Heath Lodge Vet. Group, St Bernard's Rd, ST ALBANS, Herts, AL3 5RA
Tel - 01727 835294   Spec. in poultry
                                    Avian
                                    P.M.'s

LANCS
Mr A P Raftery, 221 Upper Chorlton Road, MANCHESTER, M16 0DE
Tel - 0161 881 6868   Avian
                                    P.M.'s

S M F Jennings, Manchester Street Vet. Surg, Manchester St, OLDHAM, OL8 1UF
Tel - 0161 624 4596   Avian
                                    P.M.'s

Alan Pearson, Morningside, 30 Bonds Lane, GARSTANG, Preston
Tel - 01995 24599   Unsure

LEICS
Meadow Lane Vet. Centre, 9 Meadow Lane, LOUGHBOROUGH, Leics, LE11 1JU
Tel - 01509 212437   Avian
                                    P.M.'s

LINCOLNSHIRE
C Harding, Horncastle Lab. Southwell Lane, HORNCASTLE, Lincs, LN9 5DT
Tel - 01507 523276   Spec. in poultry
                                    P.M.'s

LONDON
K A Whitcomb, 14 Portland Road, LONDON, W11
Tel - 0171 727 2204   Poultry - Interest in no specialist qual.
                                    Avian
                                    P.M.'s

C Hall, 15 Temple Sheen Road, SHEEN, SW14 7PX
Tel - 0181 876 9696   Avian
                             P.M.'s

NORFOLK
G R Duncan, Large Animal Office, 40 Yarmouth Road, NORTH WALSHAM,
NR28 9AT
Tel - 01692 407040   Spec. in poultry
                            Avian
                            P.M.'s

S.A.Lister BSc B.Vet. Med. MRCVS. J Saverzapf, Chapelfield Vet. Partnership,
McLintock House, 21 Chapelfield Rd,
NORWICH, NR2 1RR
Tel - 01603 629046 /7/8/9.   Spec. in poultry
                             Avian
                             P.M.'s

J Saverzapf, Chapelfield Veterinary Partnership, McLintock House, 21 Chapelfield House, NORWICH, NR2 1RR
Tel - 01603 629046   Spec. in poultry
                            Avian
                            P.M.'s

OXON
Aylmer & Cannon, Vet. Hospital, Albion St, CHIPPING NORTON, Oxon, OX7 5BN
Tel - 01608 642547   Spec. in poultry
                            Avian
                            P.M.'s

SOMERSET
A J Parsons, Tower Hill Road, CREWEKERNE, Somerset, TA18 8EQ
Tel - 01460 72443   Avian
                            P.M.'s

SUSSEX
O Swarbrick, Denmans Lane, Fontwell, ARUNDEL, Sussex, BN18 0SU
Tel - 01243 682300   Spec. in poultry
                            Avian
                            P.M.'s

D C Lang, Cliffe Vet. Group, 21 Cliffe High St, LEWES, E Sussex, BN7 2AH
Tel - 01273 473232   Avian
                            P.M.'s

Howe & Starnes, Fairfield House, UCKFIELD, E Sussex, TN22 5DE
Tel - 01825 764268　　　　　　Spec. in poultry
　　　　　　　　　　　　　　　Avian
　　　　　　　　　　　　　　　P.M.'s

WARKS
S D J Marston, 94/6 King Street, BEDWORTH, Warks CV12 8JF
Tel - 01203 312193　　　　　　Deal with poultry
　　　　　　　　　　　　　　　Avian

WILTS
D G Parsons, 10 Indus Acre, Avro Way, Bowerhill, MELKSHAM, Wilts, SN12 6TP
Tel - 01225 790090　　　　　　Spec. in poultry
　　　　　　　　　　　　　　　Avian
　　　　　　　　　　　　　　　P.M.'s

WORCS
J C Waine, 97 Mount Pleasant, REDDITCH, Worcs, B97 4JD
Tel - 01527 550111　　　　　　Avian
　　　　　　　　　　　　　　　P.M.'s

YORKSHIRE
A G Greenwood, Int. Zoo Vet. Grp, Keighley Bus. Centre, South St, KEIGHLEY,
W Yorks, BD21 1AG
Tel - 01535 692000　　　　　　Avian

Mr G Grant, The Vet. Surgery, Salisbury Road, YORK, YO2 4YN
Tel - 01904 643997　　　　　　Spec. in poultry
　　　　　　　　　　　　　　　Avian
　　　　　　　　　　　　　　　P.M.'s

WALES

GWYNEDD
E Barbour-Hill, Tan y Coed, Penlon, High Street, BANGOR, Gwynedd, LL57 1PX
Tel - 01248 355674　　　　　　Avian interest
　　　　　　　　　　　　　　　P.M.'s

Tudor Lawson & Dallimore, Bala Road, DOLGELLAU, Gwynedd, LL40 2YF
Tel - 01341 422212　　　　　　Avian
　　　　　　　　　　　　　　　P.M.'s

CLWYD
Dr John Baker, The Dormie, Bertha-Dou, RHOSEMOR, Clwyd, CH7 6PS
Tel - 01352 780307　　　　　　P.M's on cage birds only

John Parry Hickerton, Rhianfa Vet. Centre, 83 Russell Rd, RHYL, Clwyd, LL18 3DR
Tel - 01745 332553   Spec. in poultry
                            Avian
                            P.M.'s

SCOTLAND

ABERDEENSHIRE
Laurence T A Brain, The Vet. Clinic, 36 High Street, New Deer, TURRIFF, Aberdeenshire AB53 6SX
Tel - 01771 644205   P.M.'s

EDINBURGH
G J Waterall, Almond Vet. Centre, 89 Colinton Rd, EDINBURGH, EH10 5DF
Tel - 0131 337 1471   Avian

AYR
Mr Tom Pennycott, SAC Vet. Services, Avian Health Unit, AUCHINCRUIVE, Ayr KA6 5AE
Tel - 01292 520318   Spec. in poultry
                            Avian
                            P.M.'s

FIFE
W A Law, Inchcolm Vet. Services, 36 The Wynd, DALGETY BAY, Fife, KY11 5SJ
Tel - 01383 823178   Spec. in poultry

WE ARE ALWAYS DELIGHTED TO HEAR FROM ANY AVIAN VETS WHO
HAVE NOT BEEN INCLUDED ON THIS LIST

NOTES

This bird has had a Ventriculectomy (a gizzard removal!!)

NOTES

NOTES

NOTES

NOTES

NOTES

NOTES